∴ MOONBEAMS ∴
FROM THE LARGER LUNACY

BY STEPHEN LEACOCK

BEHIND THE BEYOND

NONSENSE NOVELS

LITERARY LAPSES

SUNSHINE SKETCHES

ARCADIAN
ADVENTURES WITH
THE IDLE RICH

THE MARIONETTES'
CALENDAR AND
ENGAGEMENT BOOK
1916
With Drawings by A. H. Fish

MOONBEAMS
FROM THE
LARGER LUNACY

BY STEPHEN LEACOCK

AUTHOR OF "NONSENSE NOVELS," "ARCADIAN ADVENTURES WITH THE IDLE RICH," "BEHIND THE BEYOND," ETC. . . . .

A 2992

NEW YORK: JOHN LANE COMPANY
LONDON: JOHN LANE, THE BODLEY HEAD
TORONTO: S. B. GUNDY: MCMXV

PREFACE

The prudent husbandman, after having taken from his field all the straw that is there, rakes it over with a wooden rake and gets as much again. The wise child, after the lemonade jug is empty, takes the lemons from the bottom of it and squeezes them into a still larger brew. So does the sagacious author, after having sold his material to the magazines and been paid for it, clap it into book-covers and give it another squeeze. But in the present case the author is of a nice conscience and anxious to place responsibility where it is due. He therefore wishes to make all proper acknowledgments to the editors of *Vanity Fair*, *The American Magazine*, *The Popular Magazine*, *Life*, *Puck*, *The Century*, *Methuen's Annual*, and all others who are in any way implicated in the making of this book.

STEPHEN LEACOCK.

McGill University,
    Montreal.
    Oct. 1, 1915.

CONTENTS

Contents

SPOOF. A SAMPLE OF A
THOUSAND-GUINEA NOVEL

I.—*Spoof.* *A   Thousand-Guinea Novel.   New!   Fascinating! Perplexing!*

CHAPTER I

READERS are requested to note that this novel has taken our special prize of a cheque for a thousand guineas. This alone guarantees for all intelligent readers a palpitating interest in every line of it. Among the thousands of MSS. which reached us—many of them coming in carts early in the morning, and moving in a dense phalanx, indistinguishable from the Covent Garden Market waggons; others pouring down our coal-chute during the working hours of the day; and others again being slipped surreptitiously into our letter-box by pale, timid girls, scarcely more than children, after nightfall (in fact many of them came in their nightgowns),—this manuscript alone was the sole one—in fact the only one—to receive the prize of a cheque of a thousand guineas. To other competitors we may have given, inadvertently perhaps, a bag of sovereigns or a string of pearls, but to this story alone is awarded the first prize by the unanimous decision of our judges.

When we say that the latter body included two members of the Cabinet, two Lords of the Admiralty, and two bishops, with power in case of dispute to send all the MSS. to the Czar of Russia, our readers will breathe a sigh of relief to learn that the decision was instant and unanimous. Each one of them, in reply to our telegram, answered immediately SPOOF.

This novel represents the last word in up-to-date fiction. It is well known that the modern novel has got far beyond the point of mere story-telling. The childish attempt to *interest* the reader has long since been abandoned by all the best writers. They refuse to do it. The modern novel must convey a message, or else it must paint a picture, or remove a veil, or open a new chapter in human psychology. Otherwise it is no good. SPOOF does all of these things.⟩ The reader rises from its perusal perplexed, troubled, and yet so filled with information that rising itself is a difficulty.

We cannot, for obvious reasons, insert the whole of the first chapter. But the portion here presented was praised by *The Saturday Afternoon Review* as giving one of the most graphic and at the same time realistic pictures of America ever written in fiction.

Of the characters whom our readers are to imagine seated on the deck—on one of the many decks (all connected by elevators)—of the *Gloritania,* one word may be said. Vere de Lancy is (as the reviewers have under oath declared) a typical young Englishman of the upper class. He is nephew to the Duke of ——, but of this fact no one on the ship, except the captain, the purser, the steward, and the passengers are, or is, aware.

In order entirely to conceal his identity, Vere de Lancy is travelling under the assumed name of Lancy de Vere. In order the better to hide the object of his journey, Lancy de Vere (as we shall now call him, though our readers will be able at any moment to turn his name backwards) has given it to be understood that he is travelling merely as a gentleman anxious to see America. This naturally baffles all those in contact with him.

The girl at his side—but perhaps we may best let her speak for herself.

. . . . . .

Somehow as they sat together on the deck of the great steamer in the afterglow of the sunken sun, listening to the throbbing of the propeller (a rare sound which neither of them of course had ever heard before), de Vere felt that he must speak to her. Something of the mystery of the girl fascinated him. What was she doing here alone with no one but her mother and her maid, on the bosom of the Atlantic? Why was she here? Why was she not somewhere else? The thing puzzled, perplexed him. It would not let him alone. It fastened upon his brain. Somehow he felt that if he tried to drive it away, it might nip him in the ankle.

In the end he spoke.

"And you, too," he said, leaning over her deck-chair, "are going to America?"

He had suspected this ever since the boat left Liverpool. Now at length he framed his growing conviction into words.

"Yes," she assented, and then timidly, "it is 3,213 miles wide, is it not?"

"Yes," he said, "and 1,781 miles deep! It reaches from the forty-ninth parallel to the Gulf of Mexico."

"Oh," cried the girl, "what a vivid picture! I seem to see it."

"Its major axis," he went on, his voice sinking almost to a caress, "is formed by the Rocky Mountains, which are practically a prolongation of the Cordilleran Range. It is drained," he continued——

"How splendid!" said the girl.

"Yes, is it not? It is drained by the Mississippi, by the St. Lawrence, and—dare I say it?—by the Upper Colorado."

15

Somehow his hand had found hers in the half gloaming, but she did not check him.

"Go on," she said very simply; "I think I ought to hear it."

"The great central plain of the interior," he continued, "is formed by a vast alluvial deposit carried down as silt by the Mississippi. East of this the range of the Alleghanies, nowhere more than eight thousand feet in height, forms a secondary or subordinate axis from which the watershed falls to the Atlantic."

He was speaking very quietly but earnestly. No man had ever spoken to her like this before.

"What a wonderful picture!" she murmured half to herself, half aloud, and half not aloud and half not to herself.

"Through the whole of it," de Vere went on, "there run railways, most of them from east to west, though a few run from west to east. The Pennsylvania system alone has twenty-one thousand miles of track."

"Twenty-one thousand miles," she repeated;

already she felt her will strangely subordinate to his.

He was holding her hand firmly clasped in his and looking into her face.

"Dare I tell you," he whispered, "how many employees it has?"

"Yes," she gasped, unable to resist.

"A hundred and fourteen thousand," he said.

There was silence. They were both thinking. Presently she spoke, timidly.

"Are there any cities there?"

"Cities!" he said enthusiastically, "ah, yes! let me try to give you a word-picture of them. Vast cities—with tall buildings, reaching to the very sky. Why, for instance, the new Woolworth Building in New York——"

"Yes, yes," she broke in quickly, "how high is it?"

"Seven hundred and fifty feet."

The girl turned and faced him.

"Don't," she said. "I can't bear it. Some other time, perhaps, but not now."

She had risen and was gathering up her wraps. "And you," she said, "why are you going to America?"

"Why?" he answered. "Because I want to see, to know, to learn. And when I have learned and seen and known, I want other people to see and to learn and to know. I want to write it all down, all the vast palpitating picture of it. Ah! if I only could—I want to see" (and here he passed his hand through his hair as if trying to remember) "something of the relations of labour and capital, of the extraordinary development of industrial machinery, of the new and intricate organisation of corporation finance, and in particular I want to try to analyse—no one has ever done it yet— the men who guide and drive it all. I want to set down the psychology of the multimillionaire!"

He paused. The girl stood irresolute. She was thinking (apparently, for if not, why stand there?).

"Perhaps," she faltered, "I could help you."

"You!"

"Yes, I might." She hesitated. "I—I—come from America."

"You!" said de Vere in astonishment. "With a face and voice like yours! It is impossible!"

The boldness of the compliment held her speechless for a moment.

"I do," she said; "my people lived just outside of Cohoes."

"They couldn't have," he said passionately.

"I shouldn't speak to you like this," the girl went on, "but it's because I feel from what you have said that you know and love America. And I think I can help you."

"You mean," he said, divining her idea, "that you can help me to meet a multimillionaire?"

"Yes," she answered, still hesitating.

"You know one?"

"Yes," still hesitating, "I know *one.*"

She seemed about to say more, her lips had already opened, when suddenly the dull raucous blast of the foghorn (they used a raucous one on this ship on purpose) cut the night air. Wet fog rolled in about them, wetting everything.

The girl shivered.

"I must go," she said; "good night."

For a moment de Vere was about to detain her. The wild thought leaped to his mind to ask her her name or at least her mother's. With a powerful effort he checked himself.

"Good night," he said.

She was gone.

CHAPTER II

LIMITS of space forbid the insertion of the whole of this chapter. Its opening contains one of the most vivid word-pictures of the inside of an American customs house ever pictured in words. From the customs wharf de Vere is driven in a taxi to the Belmont. Here he engages a room; here, too, he sleeps; here also, though cautiously at first, he eats. All this is so admirably described that only those who have driven in a taxi to an hotel and slept there can hope to appreciate it.

Limits of space also forbid our describing in

full de Vere's vain quest in New York of the beautiful creature whom he had met on the steamer and whom he had lost from sight in the aigrette department of the customs house. A thousand times he cursed his folly in not having asked her name.

Meanwhile no word comes from her, till suddenly, mysteriously, unexpectedly, on the fourth day a note is handed to de Vere by the Third Assistant Head Waiter of the Belmont. It is addressed in a lady's hand. He tears it open. It contains only the written words, *"Call on Mr. J. Superman Overgold. He is a multimillionaire. He expects you."*

To leap into a taxi (from the third story of the Belmont) was the work of a moment. To drive to the office of Mr. Overgold was less. The portion of the novel which follows is perhaps the most notable part of it. It is this part of the chapter which the *Hibbert Journal* declares to be the best piece of psychological analysis that appears in any novel of the season. We reproduce it here.

. . . .

21

"Exactly, exactly," said de Vere, writing rapidly in his note-book as he sat in one of the deep leather armchairs of the luxurious office of Mr. Overgold. "So you sometimes feel as if the whole thing were not worth while."

"I do," said Mr. Overgold. "I can't help asking myself what it all means. Is life, after all, merely a series of immaterial phenomena, self-developing and based solely on sensation and reaction, or is it something else?"

He paused for a moment to sign a cheque for $10,000 and throw it out of the window, and then went on, speaking still with the terse brevity of a man of business.

"Is sensation everywhere or is there perception too? On what grounds, if any, may the hypothesis of a self-explanatory consciousness be rejected? In how far are we warranted in supposing that innate ideas are inconsistent with pure materialism?"

De Vere listened, fascinated. Fortunately for himself, he was a University man, fresh from the examination halls of his Alma Mater. He was able to respond at once.

"I think," he said modestly, "I grasp your thought. You mean—to what extent are we prepared to endorse Hegel's dictum of immaterial evolution?"

"Exactly," said Mr. Overgold. "How far, if at all, do we substantiate the Kantian hypothesis of the transcendental?"

"Precisely," said de Vere eagerly. "And for what reasons [naming them] must we reject Spencer's theory of the unknowable?"

"Entirely so," continued Mr. Overgold. "And why, if at all, does Bergsonian illusionism differ from pure nothingness?"

They both paused.

Mr. Overgold had risen. There was great weariness in his manner.

"It saddens one, does it not?" he said.

He had picked up a bundle of Panama two per cent. gold bonds and was looking at them in contempt.

"The emptiness of it all!" he muttered. He extended the bonds to de Vere.

"Do you want them," he said, "or shall I throw them away?"

23

"Give them to me," said de Vere quietly; "they are not worth the throwing."

"No, no," said Mr. Overgold, speaking half to himself, as he replaced the bonds in his desk. "It is a burden that I must carry alone. I have no right to ask any one to share it. But come," he continued, "I fear I am sadly lacking in the duties of international hospitality. I am forgetting what I owe to Anglo-American courtesy. I am neglecting the new obligations of our common Indo-Chinese policy. My motor is at the door. Pray let me take you to my house to lunch."

De Vere assented readily, telephoned to the Belmont not to keep lunch waiting for him, and in a moment was speeding up the magnificent Riverside Drive towards Mr. Overgold's home. On the way Mr. Overgold pointed out various objects of interest,—Grant's tomb, Lincoln's tomb, Edgar Allan Poe's grave, the ticket office of the New York Subway, and various other points of historic importance.

On arriving at the house, de Vere was ushered up a flight of broad marble steps to a hall fitted on every side with almost priceless *objets d'art* and others, ushered to the cloak-room and out of it, butlered into the lunch-room and footmanned to a chair.

As they entered, a lady already seated at the table turned to meet them.

One glance was enough—plenty.

It was she—the object of de Vere's impas-sioned quest. A rich lunch-gown was girdled about her with a twelve-o'clock band of pearls.

She reached out her hand, smiling.

"Dorothea," said the multimillionaire, "this is Mr. de Vere. Mr. de Vere—my wife."

CHAPTER III

OF this next chapter we need only say that the *Blue Review* (Adults Only) declares it to be the most daring and yet conscientious han-dling of the sex-problem ever attempted and done. The fact that the *Congregational Times* declares that this chapter will undermine the whole foundations of English Society and let it fall, we pass over: we hold certificates in writing from a great number of the Anglican clergy, to the effect that they have carefully read the entire novel and see nothing in it.

. . . .

They stood looking at one another.

"So you didn't know," she murmured.

In a flash de Vere realised that she hadn't known that he didn't know and knew now that he knew.

He found no words.

The situation was a tense one. Nothing but the woman's innate tact could save it. Dorothea Overgold rose to it with the dignity of a queen.

She turned to her husband.

"Take your soup over to the window," she said, "and eat it there."

The millionaire took his soup to the window and sat beneath a little palm tree, eating it.

"You didn't know," she repeated.

"No," said de Vere; "how could I?"

"And yet," she went on, "you loved me, although you didn't know that I was married?"

"Yes," answered de Vere simply. "I loved you, in spite of it."

"How splendid!" she said.

There was a moment's silence. Mr. Overgold had returned to the table, the empty plate in his hand. His wife turned to him again with the same unfailing tact.

"Take your asparagus to the billiard-room," she said, "and eat it there."

"Does he know, too?" asked de Vere.

"Mr. Overgold?" she said carelessly. "I suppose he does. *Eh après, mon ami?*"

French? Another mystery! Where and how had she learned it? de Vere asked himself. Not in France, certainly.

"I fear that you are very young, *amico mio*," Dorothea went on carelessly. "After all, what is there wrong in it, *piccolo pochito?* To a man's mind perhaps—but to a woman, love is love."

She beckoned to the butler.

"Take Mr. Overgold a cutlet to the music-room," she said, "and give him his gorgonzola on the inkstand in the library."

27

"And now," she went on, in that caressing way which seemed so natural to her, "don't let us think about it any more! After all, what is is, isn't it?"

"I suppose it is," said de Vere, half convinced in spite of himself.

"Or at any rate," said Dorothea, "nothing can at the same time both be and not be. But come," she broke off, gaily dipping a macaroon in a glass of *crème de menthe* and offering it to him with a pretty gesture of camaraderie, "don't let's be gloomy any more. I want to take you with me to the matinée."

"Is he coming?" asked de Vere, pointing at Mr. Overgold's empty chair.

"Silly boy," laughed Dorothea. "Of course John is coming. You surely don't want to buy the tickets yourself."

.   .   .   .

The days that followed brought a strange new life to de Vere.

Dorothea was ever at his side. At the theatre, at the polo ground, in the park, everywhere they were together. And with them was Mr. Overgold.

The three were always together. At times at the theatre Dorothea and de Vere would sit downstairs and Mr. Overgold in the gallery; at other times, de Vere and Mr. Overgold would sit in the gallery and Dorothea downstairs; at times one of them would sit in Row A, another in Row B, and a third in Row C; at other times two would sit in Row B and one in Row C; at the opera, at times, one of the three would sit listening, the others talking, at other times two listening and one talking, and at other times three talking and none listening.

Thus the three formed together one of the most perplexing, maddening triangles that ever disturbed the society of the metropolis.

.   .   .   .

The *dénouement* was bound to come.

It came.

It was late at night.

De Vere was standing beside Dorothea in the brilliantly lighted hall of the Grand Palaver Hotel, where they had had supper. Mr. Overgold was busy for a moment at the cashier's desk.

"Dorothea," de Vere whispered passionately, "I want to take you away, away from all this. I want you."

She turned and looked him full in the face. Then she put her hand in his, smiling bravely.

"I will come," she said.

"Listen," he went on, "the *Gloritania* sails for England to-morrow at midnight. I have everything ready. Will you come?"

"Yes," she answered, "I will"; and then passionately, "Dearest, I will follow you to England, to Liverpool, to the end of the earth."

She paused in thought a moment and then added.

"Come to the house just before midnight. William, the second chauffeur (he is devoted to me), shall be at the door with the third car. The fourth footman will bring my things —I can rely on him; the fifth housemaid can have them all ready—she would never betray me. I will have the undergardener—the sixth

—waiting at the iron gate to let you in; he would die rather than fail me."

She paused again—then she went on.

"There is only one thing, dearest, that I want to ask. It is not much. I hardly think you would refuse it at such an hour. May I bring my husband with me?"

De Vere's face blanched.

"Must you?" he said.

"I think I must," said Dorothea. "You don't know how I've grown to value, to lean upon, him. At times I have felt as if I always wanted him to be near me; I like to feel wherever I am—at the play, at a restaurant, anywhere—that I can reach out and touch him. I know," she continued, "that it's only a wild fancy and that others would laugh at it, but you can understand, can you not—*carino caruso mio?* And think, darling, in our new life, how busy he, too, will be—making money for all of us—in a new money market. It's just wonderful how he does it."

A great light of renunciation lit up de Vere's face.

"Bring him," he said.

"I knew that you would say that," she murmured, "and listen, *pochito* pocket-edition, may I ask one thing more, one weeny thing? William, the second chauffeur—I think he would fade away if I were gone—may I bring him, too? Yes! O my darling, how can I repay you? And the second footman, and the third housemaid—if I were gone I fear that none of——"

"Bring them all," said de Vere half bitterly; "we will all elope together."

And as he spoke Mr. Overgold sauntered over from the cashier's desk, his open purse still in his hand, and joined them. There was a dreamy look upon his face.

"I wonder," he murmured, "whether personality survives or whether it, too, when up against the irresistible, dissolves and resolves itself into a series of negative reactions?"

De Vere's empty heart echoed the words.

Then they passed out and the night swallowed them up.

CHAPTER IV

AT a little before midnight on the next night,
two motors filled with muffled human beings
might have been perceived, or seen, moving
noiselessly from Riverside Drive to the steamer
wharf where lay the *Gloritania.*

A night of intense darkness enveloped the
Hudson. Outside the inside of the dockside a
defense fog wrapped the Statue of Liberty. Beside the steamer customs officers and deportation officials moved silently to and fro in long
black cloaks, carrying little deportation lan-
terns in their hands.

To these Mr. Overgold presented in silence
his deportation certificates, granting his party
permission to leave the United States under
the imbecility clause of the Interstate Commerce Act.

No objection was raised.

A few moments later the huge steamer was
slipping away in the darkness.

On its deck a little group of people, standing

33

beside a pile of first-class cabin luggage, directed a last sad look through their heavy black disguise at the rapidly vanishing shore which they could not see.

De Vere, who stood in the midst of them, clasping their hands, thus stood and gazed his last at America.

"Spoof!" he said.

(We admit that this final panorama, weird in its midnight mystery, and filling the mind of the reader with a sense of something like awe, is only appended to *Spoof* in order to coax him to read our forthcoming sequel, *Spiff*!)

34

THE READING PUBLIC

II.—The Reading Public. A Book Store Study

WISH to look about the store? Oh, oh, by all means, sir," he said.

Then as he rubbed his hands together in an urbane fashion he directed a piercing glance at me through his spectacles.

"You'll find some things that might interest you," he said, "in the back of the store on the left. We have there a series of reprints—*Universal Knowledge from Aristotle to Arthur Balfour*—at seventeen cents. Or perhaps you might like to look over the *Pantheon of Dead Authors* at ten cents. Mr. Sparrow," he called, "just show this gentleman our classical reprints—the ten-cent series."

With that he waved his hand to an assistant and dismissed me from his thought.

In other words, he had divined me in a moment. There was no use in my having bought a sage-green fedora in Broadway, and a sporting tie done up crosswise with spots as big as nickels. These little adornments can never hide the soul within. I was a professor, and he knew it, or at least, as part of his business, he could divine it on the instant.

The sales manager of the biggest book store for ten blocks cannot be deceived in a customer. And he knew, of course, that, as a professor, I was no good. I had come to the store, as all professors go to book stores, just as a wasp comes to an open jar of marmalade. He knew that I would hang around for two hours, get in everybody's way, and finally buy a cheap reprint of the *Dialogues of Plato,* or the *Prose Works of John Milton,* or *Locke on the Human Understanding,* or some trash of that sort.

As for real taste in literature—the ability to appreciate at its worth a dollar-fifty novel of last month, in a spring jacket with a tango frontispiece—I hadn't got it and he knew it.

He despised me, of course. But it is a
38

maxim of the book business that a professor standing up in a corner buried in a book looks well in a store. The real customers like it.

So it was that even so up-to-date a manager as Mr. Sellyer tolerated my presence in a back corner of his store: and so it was that I had an opportunity of noting something of his methods with his real customers—methods so successful, I may say, that he is rightly looked upon by all the publishing business as one of the mainstays of literature in America.

I had no intention of standing in the place and listening as a spy. In fact, to tell the truth, I had become immediately interested in a new translation of the *Moral Discourses of Epictetus*. The book was very neatly printed, quite well bound and was offered at eighteen cents; so that for the moment I was strongly tempted to buy it, though it seemed best to take a dip into it first.

I had hardly read more than the first three chapters when my attention was diverted by a conversation going on in the front of the store.

"You're quite sure it's his *latest?*" a fash-

ionably dressed lady was saying to Mr. Sellyer.

"Oh, yes, Mrs. Rasselyer," answered the
manager. "I assure you this is his very latest.
In fact, they only came in yesterday."

As he spoke, he indicated with his hand a
huge pile of books, gayly jacketed in white and
blue. I could make out the title in big gilt
lettering—*GOLDEN DREAMS*.

"Oh, yes," repeated Mr. Sellyer. "This is
Mr. Slush's latest book. It's having a wonderful sale."

"That's all right, then," said the lady. "You
see, one sometimes gets taken in so: I came in
here last week and took two that seemed very
nice, and I never noticed till I got home that
they were both old books, published, I think,
six months ago."

"Oh, dear me, Mrs. Rasselyer," said the
manager in an apologetic tone, "I'm extremely
sorry. Pray let us send for them and exchange
them for you."

"Oh, it does not matter," said the lady; "of
course I didn't read them. I gave them to my

40

maid. She probably wouldn't know the differ-
ence, anyway."

"I suppose not," said Mr. Sellyer, with a
condescending smile. "But of course, madam," he went on, falling into the easy chat of
the fashionable bookman, "such mistakes are
bound to happen sometimes. We had a very
painful case only yesterday. One of our oldest
customers came in in a great hurry to buy
books to take on the steamer, and before we
realised what he had done—selecting the books
I suppose merely by the titles, as some gentlemen are apt to do—he had taken two of last
year's books. We wired at once to the steamer,
but I'm afraid it's too late."

"But now, this book," said the lady, idly
turning over the leaves, "is it good? What is
it about?"

"It's an extremely *powerful* thing," said Mr.
Sellyer, "in fact, *masterly*. The critics are saying that it's perhaps *the* most powerful book
of the season. It has a——" and here Mr.
Sellyer paused, and somehow his manner re-
minded me of my own when I am explaining

41

to a university class something that I don't know myself—"It has a—a—*power,* so to speak—a very exceptional power; in fact, one may say without exaggeration it is the most *powerful* book of the month. Indeed," he added, getting on to easier ground, "it's having a perfectly wonderful sale."

"You seem to have a great many of them," said the lady.

"Oh, we have to," answered the manager. "There's a regular rush on the book. Indeed, you know it's a book that is bound to make a sensation. In fact, in certain quarters, they are saying that it's a book that ought not to——" And here Mr. Sellyer's voice became so low and ingratiating that I couldn't hear the rest of the sentence.

"Oh, really!" said Mrs. Rasselyer. "Well, I think I'll take it then. One ought to see what these talked-of things are about, anyway."

She had already begun to button her gloves, and to readjust her feather boa with which she had been knocking the Easter cards off the counter. Then she suddenly remembered something.

"Oh, I was forgetting," she said. "Will you send something to the house for Mr. Rasselyer at the same time? He's going down to Virginia for the vacation. You know the kind of thing he likes, do you not?"

"Oh, perfectly, madam," said the manager. "Mr. Rasselyer generally reads works of—er —I think he buys mostly books on—er——"

"Oh, travel and that sort of thing," said the lady.

"Precisely. I think we have here," and he pointed to the counter on the left, "what Mr. Rasselyer wants."

He indicated a row of handsome books— *"Seven Weeks in the Sahara,* seven dollars; *Six Months in a Waggon,* six-fifty net; *Afternoons in an Oxcart,* two volumes, four-thirty, with twenty off."

"I think he has read those," said Mrs. Rasselyer. "At least there are a good many at home that seem like that."

"Oh, very possibly—but here, now, *Among*

43

the Cannibals of Corfu—yes, that I think he
has had—*Among the*—that, too, I think—but
this I am certain he would like, just in this
morning—*Among the Monkeys of New Guinea*
—ten dollars, net."

And with this Mr. Sellyer laid his hand on a
pile of new books, apparently as numerous as
the huge pile of *Golden Dreams*.

"Among the Monkeys," he repeated, almost
caressingly.

"It seems rather expensive," said the lady.

"Oh, very much so—a most expensive book,"
the manager repeated in a tone of enthusiasm.
"You see, Mrs. Rasselyer, it's the illustrations,
actual photographs"—he ran the leaves over
in his fingers—"of actual monkeys, taken with
the camera—and the paper, you notice—in
fact, madam, the book costs, the mere manufacture of it, nine dollars and ninety cents—
of course we make no profit on it. But it's a
book we like to handle."

Everybody likes to be taken into the details
of technical business; and of course everybody
likes to know that a bookseller is losing money.

These, I realised, were two axioms in the methods of Mr. Sellyer.

So very naturally Mrs. Rasselyer bought *Among the Monkeys,* and in another moment Mr. Sellyer was directing a clerk to write down an address on Fifth Avenue, and was bowing deeply as he showed the lady out of the door.

As he turned back to his counter his manner seemed much changed.

"That Monkey book," I heard him murmur to his assistant, "is going to be a pretty stiff proposition."

But he had no time for further speculation. Another lady entered.

This time even to an eye less trained than Mr. Sellyer's, the deep, expensive mourning and the pensive face proclaimed the sentimental widow.

"Something new in fiction," repeated the manager, "yes, madam—here's a charming thing—*Golden Dreams*"—he hung lovingly on the words—"a very sweet story, singularly sweet; in fact, madam, the critics are saying it is the sweetest thing that Mr. Slush has done."

"Is it good?" said the lady. I began to realise that all customers asked this.

"A charming book," said the manager. "It's a love story—very simple and sweet, yet wonderfully charming. Indeed, the reviews say it's the most charming book of the month. My wife was reading it aloud only last night. She could hardly read for tears."

"I suppose it's quite a safe book, is it?" asked the widow. "I want it for my little daughter."

"Oh, quite safe," said Mr. Sellyer, with an almost parental tone, "in fact, written quite in the old style, like the dear old books of the past—quite like"—here Mr. Sellyer paused with a certain slight haze of doubt visible in his eye—"like Dickens and Fielding and Sterne and so on. We sell a great many to the clergy, madam."

The lady bought *Golden Dreams*, received it wrapped up in green enamelled paper, and passed out.

"Have you any good light reading for vacation time?" called out the next customer in a loud, breezy voice—he had the air of a stock broker starting on a holiday.

"Yes," said Mr. Sellyer, and his face almost broke into a laugh as he answered, "here's an excellent thing—*Golden Dreams*—quite the most humorous book of the season—simply screaming—my wife was reading it aloud only yesterday. She could hardly read for laughing."

"What's the price, one dollar? One-fifty. All right, wrap it up." There was a clink of money on the counter, and the customer was gone. I began to see exactly where professors and college people who want copies of *Epictetus* at 18 cents and sections of *World Reprints of Literature* at 12 cents a section come in, in the book trade.

"Yes, Judge!" said the manager to the next customer, a huge, dignified personage in a wide-awake hat, "sea stories? Certainly. Excellent reading, no doubt, when the brain is overcharged as yours must be. Here is the very latest—*Among the Monkeys of New Guinea*, ten dollars, reduced to four-fifty. The manufacture alone costs six-eighty. We're selling it out. Thank you, Judge. Send it? Yes. Good morning."

After that the customers came and went in a string. I noticed that though the store was filled with books—ten thousand of them, at a guess—Mr. Sellyer was apparently only selling two. Every woman who entered went away with *Golden Dreams:* every man was given a copy of the *Monkeys of New Guinea.* To one lady *Golden Dreams* was sold as exactly the reading for a holiday, to another as the very book to read *after* a holiday; another bought it as a book for a rainy day, and a fourth as the right sort of reading for a fine day. The *Monkeys* was sold as a sea story, a land story, a story of the jungle, and a story of the mountains, and it was put at a price corresponding to Mr. Sellyer's estimate of the purchaser.

At last after a busy two hours, the store grew empty for a moment.

"Wilfred," said Mr. Sellyer, turning to his chief assistant, "I am going out to lunch. Keep those two books running as hard as you can.

48

We'll try them for another day and then cut them right out. And I'll drop round to Dockem & Discount, the publishers, and make a kick about them, and see what they'll do."

I felt that I had lingered long enough. I drew near with the *Epictetus* in my hand.

"Yes, sir," said Mr. Sellyer, professional again in a moment. *"Epictetus?* A charming thing. Eighteen cents. Thank you. Perhaps we have some other things there that might interest you. We have a few second-hand things in the alcove there that you might care to look at. There's an *Aristotle,* two volumes —a very fine thing—practically illegible, that you might like: and a *Cicero* came in yesterday —very choice—damaged by damp—and I think we have a *Machiavelli,* quite exceptional —practically torn to pieces, and the covers gone—a very rare old thing, sir, if you're an expert."

"No, thanks," I said. And then from a curiosity that had been growing in me and that I couldn't resist, "That book—*Golden*

Dreams," I said, "you seem to think it a very wonderful work?"

Mr. Sellyer directed one of his shrewd glances at me. He knew I didn't want to buy the book, and perhaps, like lesser people, he had his off moments of confidence.

He shook his head.

"A bad business," he said. "The publishers have unloaded the thing on us, and we have to do what we can. They're stuck with it, I understand, and they look to us to help them. They're advertising it largely and may pull it off. Of course, there's just a chance. One can't tell. It's just possible we may get the church people down on it and if so we're all right. But short of that we'll never make it. I imagine it's perfectly rotten."

"Haven't you read it?" I asked.

"Dear me, no!" said the manager. His air was that of a milkman who is offered a glass of his own milk. "A pretty time I'd have if I tried to *read* the new books. It's quite enough to keep track of them without that."

"But those people," I went on, deeply perplexed, "who bought the book. Won't they be disappointed?"

Mr. Sellyer shook his head. "Oh, no," he said; "you see, they won't *read* it. They never do."

"But at any rate," I insisted, "your wife thought it a fine story."

Mr. Sellyer smiled widely.

"I am not married, sir," he said.

AFTERNOON ADVEN-
TURES AT MY CLUB

1.—*The Anecdotes of*
Dr. So and So

THAT is not really his name. I merely call him that from his manner of talking.

His specialty is telling me short anecdotes of his professional life from day to day.

They are told with wonderful dash and power, except for one slight omission, which is, that you never know what the doctor is talking about. Beyond this, his little stories are of unsurpassed interest—but let me illustrate.

. . . .

He came into the semi-silence room of the club the other day and sat down beside me.

"Have something or other?" he said.

"No, thanks," I answered.

"Smoke anything?" he asked.

"No, thanks."

The doctor turned to me. He evidently wanted to talk.

"I've been having a rather peculiar experience," he said. "Man came to me the other day—three or four weeks ago—and said, 'Doctor, I feel out of sorts. I believe I've got so and so.' 'Ah,' I said, taking a look at him, 'been eating so and so, eh?' 'Yes,' he said. 'Very good,' I said, 'take so and so.'

"Well, off the fellow went—I thought nothing of it—simply wrote such and such in my note-book, such and such a date, symptoms such and such—prescribed such and such, and so forth, you understand?"

"Oh, yes, perfectly, doctor," I answered.

"Very good. Three days later—a ring at the bell in the evening—my servant came to the surgery. 'Mr. So and So is here. Very anxious to see you.' 'All right!' I went down. There he was, with every symptom of so and so written all over him—every symptom of it —this and this and this——"

"Awful symptoms, doctor," I said, shaking my head.

"Are they not?" he said, quite unaware that he hadn't named any. "There he was with every symptom, heart so and so, eyes so and so, pulse this—I looked at him right in the eye and I said—'Do you want me to tell you the truth?' 'Yes,' he said. 'Very good,' I answered, 'I will. You've got so and so.' He fell back as if shot. 'So and so!' he repeated, dazed. I went to the sideboard and poured him out a drink of such and such. 'Drink this,' I said. He drank it. 'Now,' I said, 'listen to what I say: You've got so and so. There's only one chance,' I said, 'you must limit your eating and drinking to such and such, you must sleep such and such, avoid every form of such and such—I'll give you a cordial, so many drops every so long, but mind you, unless you do so and so, it won't help you.' 'All right, very good.' Fellow promised. Off he went."

The doctor paused a minute and then resumed:

"Would you believe it—two nights later, I saw the fellow—after the theatre, in a restaurant—whole party of people—big plate of so

57

and so in front of him—quart bottle of so and so on ice—such and such and so forth. I stepped over to him—tapped him on the shoulder: 'See here,' I said, 'if you won't obey my instructions, you can't expect me to treat you.' I walked out of the place."

"And what happened to him?" I asked.

"Died," said the doctor, in a satisfied tone. "Died. I've just been filling in the certificate: So and so, aged such and such, died of so and so!"

"An awful disease," I murmured.

2.—*The Shattered Health of Mr. Podge*

"HOW are you, Podge?" I said, as I sat down in a leather armchair beside him.

I only meant "How-do-you-do?" but he rolled his big eyes sideways at me in his flabby face (it was easier than moving his face) and he answered:

"I'm not as well to-day as I was yesterday afternoon. Last week I was feeling pretty good part of the time, but yesterday about four o'clock the air turned humid, and I don't feel so well."

"Have a cigarette?" I said.

"No, thanks; I find they affect the bronchial toobes."

"Whose?" I asked.

"Mine," he answered.

"Oh, yes," I said, and I lighted one. "So

59

you find the weather trying," I continued cheer-fully.

"Yes, it's too humid. It's up to a satura-tion of sixty-six. I'm all right till it passes sixty-four. Yesterday afternoon it was only about sixty-one, and I felt fine. But after that it went up. I guess it must be a contraction of the epidermis pressing on some of the seba-ceous glands, don't you?"

"I'm sure it is," I said. "But why don't you just sleep it off till it's over?"

"I don't like to sleep too much," he an-swered. "I'm afraid of it developing into hypersomnia. There are cases where it's been known to grow into a sort of lethargy that pretty well stops all brain action alto-gether——"

"That would be too bad," I murmured. "What do you do to prevent it?"

"I generally drink from half to three-quar-ters of a cup of black coffee, or nearly black, every morning at from eleven to five minutes past, so as to keep off hypersomnia. It's the best thing, the doctor says."

"Aren't you afraid," I said, "of its keeping you awake?"

"I am," answered Podge, and a spasm passed over his big yellow face. "I'm always afraid of insomnia. That's the worst thing of all. The other night I went to bed about half-past ten, or twenty-five minutes after,—I forget which,—and I simply couldn't sleep. I couldn't. I read a magazine story, and I still couldn't; and I read another, and still I couldn't sleep. It scared me bad."

"Oh, pshaw," I said; "I don't think sleep matters as long as one eats properly and has a good appetite."

He shook his head very dubiously. "I ate a plate of soup at lunch," he said, "and I feel it still."

"You *feel* it!"

"Yes," repeated Podge, rolling his eyes sideways in a pathetic fashion that he had, "I still feel it. I oughtn't to have eaten it. It was some sort of a bean soup, and of course it was full of nitrogen. I oughtn't to touch nitrogen," he added, shaking his head.

"Not take any nitrogen?" I repeated.

"No, the doctor—both doctors—have told me that. I can eat starches, and albumens, all right, but I have to keep right away from all carbons and nitrogens. I've been dieting that way for two years, except that now and again I take a little glucose or phosphates."

"That must be a nice change," I said, cheerfully.

"It is," he answered in a grateful sort of tone.

There was a pause. I looked at his big twitching face, and listened to the heavy wheezing of his breath, and I felt sorry for him.

"See here, Podge," I said, "I want to give you some good advice."

"About what?"

"About your health."

"Yes, yes, do," he said. Advice about his health was right in his line. He lived on it.

"Well, then, cut out all this fool business of diet and drugs and nitrogen. Don't bother about anything of the sort. Forget it. Eat everything you want to, just when you want it. Drink all you like. Smoke all you can—and you'll feel a new man in a week."

"Say, do you think so!" he panted, his eyes filled with a new light.

"I know it," I answered. And as I left him I shook hands with a warm feeling about my heart of being a benefactor to the human race.

Next day, sure enough, Podge's usual chair at the club was empty.

"Out getting some decent exercise," I thought. "Thank Heaven!"

Nor did he come the next day, nor the next, nor for a week.

"Leading a rational life at last," I thought. "Out in the open getting a little air and sunlight, instead of sitting here howling about his stomach."

The day after that I saw Dr. Slyder in black clothes glide into the club in that peculiar manner of his, like an amateur undertaker.

"Hullo, Slyder," I called to him, "you look as solemn as if you had been to a funeral."

"I have," he said very quietly, and then added, "poor Podge!"

63

"What about him?" I asked with sudden apprehension.

"Why, he died on Tuesday," answered the doctor. "Hadn't you heard? Strangest case I've known in years. Came home suddenly one day, pitched all his medicines down the kitchen sink, ordered a couple of cases of champagne and two hundred havanas, and had his housekeeper cook a dinner like a Roman banquet! After being under treatment for two years! Lived, you know, on the narrowest margin conceivable. I told him and Silk told him—we all told him—his only chance was to keep away from every form of nitrogenous ultra-stimulants. I said to him often, 'Podge, if you touch heavy carbonized food, you're lost.'"

"Dear me," I thought to myself, "there *are* such things after all!"

"It was a marvel," continued Slyder, "that we kept him alive at all. And, of course"—here the doctor paused to ring the bell to order two Manhattan cocktails—"as soon as he touched alcohol he was done."

64

So that was the end of the valetudinarianism of Mr. Podge.

I have always considered that I killed him.

.   .   .   .

But anyway, he was a nuisance at the club.

3.—*The Amazing Travels of Mr. Yarner*

THERE was no fault to be found with Mr. Yarner till he made his trip around the world.

It was that, I think, which disturbed his brain and unfitted him for membership in the club.

.   .   .   .

"Well," he would say, as he sat ponderously down with the air of a man opening an interesting conversation, "I was just figuring it out that eleven months ago to-day I was in Pekin."

"That's odd," I said, "I was just reckoning that eleven days ago I was in Poughkeepsie."

"They don't call it Pekin over there," he said. "It's sounded Pei-Chang."

"I know," I said, "it's the same way with Poughkeepsie, they pronounce it P'Keepsie."

"The Chinese," he went on musingly, "are a strange people."

"So are the people in P'Keepsie," I added, "awfully strange."

That kind of retort would sometimes stop him, but not always. He was especially dangerous if he was found with a newspaper in his hand; because that meant that some item of foreign intelligence had gone to his brain.

Not that I should have objected to Yarner describing his travels. Any man who has bought a ticket round the world and paid for it, is entitled to that.

But it was his manner of discussion that I considered unpermissible.

Last week, for example, in an unguarded moment I fell a victim. I had been guilty of the imprudence—I forget in what connection—of speaking of lions. I realized at once that I had done wrong—lions, giraffes, elephants, rickshaws and natives of all brands, are topics to avoid in talking with a traveller.

"Speaking of lions," began Yarner.

He was right, of course; I *had* spoken of lions.

"—I shall never forget," he went on (of course, I knew he never would), "a rather bad scrape I got into in the up-country of Uganda. Imagine yourself in a wild, rolling country covered here and there with *kwas* along the sides of the *nullahs*."

I did so.

"Well," continued Yarner, "we were sitting in our tent one hot night—too hot to sleep—when all at once we heard, not ten feet in front of us, the most terrific roar that ever came from the throat of a lion."

As he said this Yarner paused to take a gulp of bubbling whiskey and soda and looked at me so ferociously that I actually shivered.

Then quite suddenly his manner cooled down in the strangest way, and his voice changed to a commonplace tone as he said,—

"Perhaps I ought to explain that we hadn't come up to the up-country looking for big game. In fact, we had been down in the down country with no idea of going higher than Mombasa.

68

Indeed, our going even to Mombasa itself was more or less an afterthought. Our first plan was to strike across from Aden to Singapore. But our second plan was to strike direct from Colombo to Karuchi—"

"And what was your *third* plan?" I asked.

"Our third plan," said Yarner deliberately, feeling that the talk was now getting really interesting, "let me see, our third plan was to cut across from Socotra to Tananarivo."

"Oh, yes," I said.

"However, all that was changed, and changed under the strangest circumstances. We were sitting, Gallon and I, on the piazza of the Galle Face Hotel in Colombo—you know the Galle Face?"

"No, I do not," I said very positively.

"Very good. Well, I was sitting on the piazza watching a snake charmer who was seated, with a boa, immediately in front of me.

"Poor Gallon was actually within two feet of the hideous reptile. All of a sudden the beast whirled itself into a coil, its eyes fastened with hideous malignity on poor Gallon, and with its head erect it emitted the most awful hiss I have heard proceed from the mouth of any living snake."

Here Yarner paused and took a long, hissing drink of whiskey and soda: and then as the malignity died out of his face——

"I should explain," he went on, very quietly, "that Gallon was not one of our original party. We had come down to Colombo from Mongolia, going by the Pekin Hankow and the Nippon Yushen Keisha."

"That, I suppose, is the best way?" I said.

"Yes. And oddly enough but for the accident of Gallon joining us, we should have gone by the Amoy, Cochin, Singapore route, which was our first plan. In fact, but for Gallon we should hardly have got through China at all. The Boxer insurrection had taken place only fourteen years before our visit, so you can imagine the awful state of the country.

"Our meeting with Gallon was thus absolutely providential. Looking back on it, I think it perhaps saved our lives. We were in Mongolia '(this, you understand, was before we reached China), and had spent the night at a small *Yak* about four versts from Kharbin, when all of a sudden, just outside the miserable hut that we were in, we heard a perfect fusillade of shots followed immediately afterwards by one of the most blood-curdling and terrifying screams I have ever imagined—"

"Oh, yes," I said, "and that was how you met Gallon. Well, I must be off."

And as I happened at that very moment to be rescued by an incoming friend, who took but little interest in lions, and even less in Yarner, I have still to learn why the lion howled so when it met Yarner. But surely the lion had reason enough.

4.—*The Spiritual Outlook of Mr. Doomer*

ONE generally saw old Mr. Doomer looking gloomily out of the windows of the library of the club. If not there, he was to be found staring sadly into the embers of a dying fire in a deserted sitting-room.

His gloom always appeared out of place as he was one of the richest of the members.

But the cause of it,—as I came to know,—was that he was perpetually concerned with thinking about the next world. In fact he spent his whole time brooding over it.

I discovered this accidentally by happening to speak to him of the recent death of Podge, one of our fellow members.

"Very sad," I said, "Podge's death."

"Ah," returned Mr. Doomer, "very shocking. He was quite unprepared to die."

"Do you think so?" I said, "I'm awfully sorry to hear it."

"Quite unprepared," he answered. "I had reason to know it as one of his executors,—everything is confusion,—nothing signed,—no proper power of attorney,—codicils drawn up in blank and never witnessed,—in short, sir, no sense apparently of the nearness of his death and of his duty to be prepared.

"I suppose," I said, "poor Podge didn't realise that he was going to die."

"Ah, that's just it," resumed Mr. Doomer with something like sternness, "a man *ought* to realise it. Every man ought to feel that at any moment,—one can't tell when,—day or night,—he may be called upon to meet his,"—Mr. Doomer paused here as if seeking a phrase—"to meet his Financial Obligations, face to face. At any time, sir, he may be hurried before the Judge,—or rather his estate may be,—before the Judge of the probate court. It is a solemn thought, sir. And yet when I come here I see about me men laughing, talking, and playing billiards, as if there would never be a

73

day when their estate would pass into the hands of their administrators and an account must be given of every cent."

"But after all," I said, trying to fall in with his mood, "death and dissolution must come to all of us."

"That's just it," he said solemnly. "They've dissolved the tobacco people, and they've dissolved the oil people and you can't tell whose turn it may be next."

Mr. Doomer was silent a moment and then resumed, speaking in a tone of humility that was almost reverential.

"And yet there is a certain preparedness for death, a certain fitness to die that we ought all to aim at. Any man can at least think solemnly of the Inheritance Tax, and reflect whether by a contract inter vivos drawn in blank he may not obtain redemption; any man if he thinks death is near may at least divest himself of his purely speculative securities and trust himself entirely to those gold bearing bonds of the great industrial corporations whose value will not readily diminish or pass away." Mr. Doomer was speaking with something like religious rapture.

"And yet what does one see?" he continued. "Men affected with fatal illness and men stricken in years occupied still with idle talk and amusements instead of reading the financial newspapers,—and at the last carried away with scarcely time perhaps to send for their brokers when it is already too late."

"It is very sad," I said.

"Very," he repeated, "and saddest of all, perhaps, is the sense of the irrevocability of death and the changes that must come after it."

We were silent a moment.

"You think of these things a great deal, Mr. Doomer?" I said.

"I do," he answered. "It may be that it is something in my temperament, I suppose one would call it a sort of spiritual mindedness. But I think of it all constantly. Often as I stand here beside the window and see these cars go by"—he indicated a passing street car —"I cannot but realise that the time will come

75

when I am no longer a managing director and wonder whether they will keep on trying to hold the dividend down by improving the rolling stock or will declare profits to inflate the securities. These mysteries beyond the grave fascinate me, sir. Death is a mysterious thing. Who for example will take my seat on the Exchange? What will happen to my majority control of the power company? I shudder to think of the changes that may happen after death in the assessment of my real estate."

"Yes," I said, "it is all beyond our control, isn't it?"

"Quite," answered Mr. Doomer; "especially of late years one feels that, a'l said and done, we are in the hands of a Higher Power, and that the State Legislature is after all supreme. It gives one a sense of smallness. It makes one feel that in these days of drastic legislation with all one's efforts the individual is lost and absorbed in the controlling power of the state legislature. Consider the words that are used in the text of the Income Tax Case, Folio Two, or the text of the Trans-Missouri Freight Decision, and think of the revelation they contain."

I left Mr. Doomer still standing beside the window, musing on the vanity of life and on things, such as the future control of freight rates, that lay beyond the grave.

I noticed as I left him how broken and aged he had come to look. It seemed as if the chafings of the spirit were wearing the body that harboured it.

.   .   .   .

It was about a month later that I learned of Mr. Doomer's death.

Dr. Slyder told me of it in the club one afternoon, over two cocktails in the sitting-room.

"A beautiful bedside," he said, "one of the most edifying that I have ever attended. I knew that Doomer was failing and of course the time came when I had to tell him.

" 'Mr. Doomer,' I said, 'all that I, all that any medical can do for you is done; you are going to die. I have to warn you that it is time for other ministrations than mine.'

77

" 'Very good,' he said faintly but firmly, 'send for my broker.'

"They sent out and fetched Jarvis,—you know him I think,—most sympathetic man and yet most business-like—he does all the firm's business with the dying,—and we two sat beside Doomer holding him up while he signed stock transfers and blank certificates.

"Once he paused and turned his eyes on Jarvis. 'Read me from the text of the State Inheritance Tax Statute,' he said. Jarvis took the book and read aloud very quietly and simply the part at the beginning—'Whenever and wheresoever it shall appear,' down to the words, 'shall be no longer a subject of judgment or appeal but shall remain in perpetual possession.'

"Doomer listened with his eyes closed. The reading seemed to bring him great comfort. When Jarvis ended he said with a sign, 'That covers it. I'll put my faith in that.' After that he was silent a moment and then said: 'I wish I had already crossed the river. Oh, to have already crossed the river and be safe on the other side.' We knew what he meant. He had always planned to move over to New Jersey. The inheritance tax is so much more liberal.

"Presently it was all done.

" 'There,' I said, 'it is finished now.'

" 'No,' he answered, 'there is still one thing. Doctor, you've been very good to me. I should like to pay your account now without it being a charge on the estate. I will pay it as'——he paused for a moment and a fit of coughing seized him, but by an effort of will he found the power to say——'cash.'

"I took the account from my pocket (I had it with me, fearing the worst), and we laid his cheque-book before him on the bed. Jarvis thinking him too faint to write tried to guide his hand as he filled in the sum. But he shook his head.

" 'The room is getting dim,' he said. 'I can see nothing but the figures.'

" 'Never mind,' said Jarvis,——much moved, 'that's enough.'

" 'Is it four hundred and thirty?' he asked faintly.

" 'Yes,' I said, and I could feel the tears rising in my eyes, 'and fifty cents.'

"After signing the cheque his mind wandered for a moment and he fell to talking, with his eyes closed, of the new federal banking law, and of the prospect of the reserve associations being able to maintain an adequate gold supply.

"Just at the last he rallied.

" 'I want,' he said in quite a firm voice, 'to do something for both of you before I die.'

" 'Yes, yes,' we said.

" 'You are both interested, are you not,' he murmured, 'in City Traction?'

" 'Yes, yes,' we said. We knew of course that he was the managing director.

"He looked at us faintly and tried to speak.

" 'Give him a cordial,' said Jarvis. But he found his voice.

" 'The value of that stock,' he said, 'is going to take a sudden——'

"His voice grew faint.

" 'Yes, yes,' I whispered, bending over him (there were tears in both our eyes), 'tell me is it going up, or going down?'

80

" 'It is going'—he murmured,—then his eyes closed—'it is going——'

" 'Yes, yes,' I said, 'which?'

" 'It is going'—he repeated feebly and then, quite suddenly he fell back on the pillows and his soul passed. And we never knew which way it was going. It was very sad. Later on, of course, after he was dead, we knew, as everybody knew, that it went down."

5.—*The Reminiscences of*
Mr. Apricot

"RATHER a cold day, isn't it?" I said as I entered the club.

The man I addressed popped his head out from behind a newspaper and I saw it was old Mr. Apricot. So I was sorry that I had spoken.

"Not so cold as the winter of 1866," he said, beaming with benevolence.

He had an egg-shaped head, bald, with some white hair fluffed about the sides of it. He had a pink face with large blue eyes, behind his spectacles, benevolent to the verge of imbecility.

"Was that a cold winter?" I asked.

"Bitter cold," he said. "I have never told you, have I, of my early experiences in life?"

"I think I have heard you mention them," I murmured, but he had already placed a detaining hand on my sleeve. "Sit down," he said. Then he continued: "Yes, it was a cold winter. I was going to say that it was the coldest I have ever experienced, but that might be an exaggeration. But it was certainly colder than any winter that *you* have ever seen, or that we ever have now, or are likely to have. In fact the winters *now* are a mere nothing,"—here Mr. Apricot looked toward the club window where the driven snow was beating in eddies against the panes,—"simply nothing. One doesn't feel them at all,"—here he turned his eyes towards the glowing fire that flamed in the open fireplace. "But when I was a boy things were very different. I have probably never mentioned to you, have I, the circumstances of my early life?"

He had, many times. But he had turned upon me the full beam of his benevolent spectacles and I was too weak to interrupt.

"My father," went on Mr. Apricot, settling back in his chair and speaking with a far-away look in his eyes, "had settled on the banks of the Wabash River——"

"Oh, yes, I know it well," I interjected.

"Not as it was *then,*" said Mr. Apricot very quickly. "At present as you, or any other thoughtless tourist sees it, it appears a broad river pouring its vast flood in all directions. At the time I speak of it was a mere stream scarcely more than a few feet in circumference. The life we led there was one of rugged isolation and of sturdy self-reliance and effort such as it is, of course, quite impossible for *you,* or any other member of this club to understand,— I may give you some idea of what I mean when I say that at that time there was no town nearer to Pittsburg than Chicago, or to St. Paul than Minneapolis——"

"Impossible!" I said.

Mr. Apricot seemed not to notice the interruption.

"There was no place nearer to Springfield than St. Louis," he went on in a peculiar sing-song voice, "and there was nothing nearer to Denver than San Francisco, nor to New Orleans than Rio Janeiro——"

He seemed as if he would go on indefinitely.

"You were speaking of your father?" I interrupted.

"My father," said Mr. Apricot, "had settled on the banks, both banks, of the Wabash. He was like so many other men of his time, a disbanded soldier, a veteran——"

"Of the Mexican War or of the Civil War?" I asked.

"Exactly," answered Mr. Apricot, hardly heeding the question,—"of the Mexican Civil War."

"Was he under Lincoln?" I asked.

"Over Lincoln," corrected Mr. Apricot gravely. And he added,—"It is always strange to me the way in which the present generation regards Abraham Lincoln. To us, of course, at the time of which I speak, Lincoln was simply one of ourselves."

"In 1866?" I asked.

"This was 1856," said Mr. Apricot. "He came often to my father's cabin, sitting down with us to our humble meal of potatoes and whiskey (we lived with a simplicity which of course you could not possibly understand), and

85

would spend the evening talking with my father over the interpretation of the Constitution of the United States. We children used to stand beside them listening open-mouthed beside the fire in our plain leather nightgowns. I shall never forget how I was thrilled when I first heard Lincoln lay down his famous theory of the territorial jurisdiction of Congress as affected by the Supreme Court decision of 1857. I was only nine years old at the time, but it thrilled me!"

"Is it possible!" I exclaimed, "how ever could you understand it?"

"Ah! my friend," said Mr. Apricot, almost sadly, "in *those* days the youth of the United States were *educated* in the real sense of the word. We children followed the decisions of the Supreme Court with breathless interest. Our books were few but they were *good*. We had nothing to read but the law reports, the agriculture reports, the weather bulletins and the almanacs. But we read them carefully from cover to cover. How few boys have the industry to do so now, and yet how many of our greatest men were educated on practically nothing else except the law reports and the almanacs. Franklin, Jefferson, Jackson, Johnson," —Mr. Apricot had relapsed into his sing-song voice, and his eye had a sort of misty perplexity in it as he went on,—"Harrison, Thomson, Peterson, Emerson——"

I thought it better to stop him.

"But you were speaking," I said, "of the winter of eighteen fifty-six."

"Of eighteen forty-six," corrected Mr. Apricot. "I shall never forget it. How distinctly I remember,—I was only a boy then, in fact a mere lad,—fighting my way to school. The snow lay in some places as deep as ten feet"— Mr. Apricot paused—"and in others twenty. But we made our way to school in spite of it. No boys of to-day,—nor, for the matter of that, even men such as you,—would think of attempting it. But we were keen, anxious to learn. Our school was our delight. Our teacher was our friend. Our books were our companions. We gladly trudged five miles to school every morning and seven miles back at night, did chores till midnight, studied algebra by candlelight"——here Mr. Apricot's voice had fallen into its characteristic sing-song, and his eyes were vacant——"rose before daylight, dressed by lamplight, fed the hogs by lantern-light, fetched the cows by twilight——"

I thought it best to stop him.

"But you did eventually get off the farm, did you not?" I asked.

"Yes," he answered, "my opportunity presently came to me as it came in those days to any boy of industry and intelligence who knocked at the door of fortune till it opened. I shall never forget how my first chance in life came to me. A man, an entire stranger, struck no doubt with the fact that I looked industrious and willing, offered me a dollar to drive a load of tan bark to the nearest market——"

"Where was that?" I asked.

"Minneapolis, seven hundred miles. But I did it. I shall never forget my feelings when I found myself in Minneapolis with one dollar in my pocket and with the world all before me."

"What did you do?" I said.

"First," said Mr. Apricot, "I laid out seventy-five cents for a suit of clothes (things were cheap in those days); for fifty cents I bought an overcoat, for twenty-five I got a hat, for ten cents a pair of boots, and with the rest of my money I took a room for a month with a Swedish family, paid a month's board with a German family, arranged to have my washing done by an Irish family, and——"

"But surely, Mr. Apricot——" I began.

.   .   .   .

But at this point the young man who is generally in attendance on old Mr. Apricot when he comes to the club, appeared on the scene.

"I am afraid," he said to me aside as Mr. Apricot was gathering up his newspapers and his belongings, "that my uncle has been rather boring you with his reminiscences."

"Not at all," I said, "he's been telling me all about his early life in his father's cabin on the Wabash——"

"I was afraid so," said the young man. "Too bad. You see he wasn't really there at all."

89

"Not there!" I said.

"No. He only fancies that he was. He was brought up in New York, and has never been west of Philadelphia. In fact he has been very well to do all his life. But he found that it counted against him: it hurt him in politics. So he got into the way of talking about the Middle West and early days there, and sometimes he forgets that he wasn't there."

"I see," I said.

Meantime Mr. Apricot was ready.

"Good-bye, good-bye," he said very cheerily, —"A delightful chat. We must have another talk over old times soon. I must tell you about my first trip over the Plains at the time when I was surveying the line of the Union Pacific. You who travel nowadays in your Pullman coaches and observation cars can have no idea——"

Come along, uncle," said the young man.

6.—*The Last Man out of Europe*

HE came into the club and shook hands with me as if he hadn't seen me for a year. In reality I had seen him only eleven months ago, and hadn't thought of him since.

"How are you, Parkins?" I said in a guarded tone, for I saw at once that there was something special in his manner.

"Have a cig?" he said as he sat down on the edge of an arm-chair, dangling his little boot.

Any young man who calls a cigarette a "cig" I despise. "No, thanks," I said.

"Try one," he went on, "they're Hungarian. They're some I managed to bring through with me out of the war zone."

As he said "war zone," his face twisted up into a sort of scowl of self-importance.

I looked at Parkins more closely and I noticed that he had on some sort of foolish little coat, short in the back, and the kind of bow-tie that they wear in the Hungarian bands of the Sixth Avenue restaurants.

Then I knew what the trouble was. He was the last man out of Europe, that is to say, the latest last man. There had been about fourteen others in the club that same afternoon. In fact they were sitting all over it in Italian suits and Viennese overcoats, striking German matches on the soles of Dutch boots. These were the "war zone" men and they had just got out "in the clothes they stood up in." Naturally they hated to change.

So I knew all that this young man, Parkins, was going to say, and all about his adventures before he began.

"Yes," he said, "we were caught right in the war zone. By Jove, I never want to go through again what I went through."

With that, he sank back into the chair in the pose of a man musing in silence over the recollection of days of horror.

I let him muse. In fact I determined to let him muse till he burst before I would ask him what he had been through. I knew it, anyway.

Presently he decided to go on talking.

"We were at Izzl," he said, "in the Carpathians, Loo Jones and I. We'd just made a walking tour from Izzl to Fryzzl and back again."

"Why did you come back?" I asked.

"Back where?"

"Back to Izzl," I explained, "after you'd once got to Fryzzl. It seems unnecessary, but, never mind, go on."

"That was in July," he continued. "There wasn't a sign of war, not a sign. We heard that Russia was beginning to mobilize," (at this word be blew a puff from his cigarette and then repeated "beginning to mobilize") "but we thought nothing of it."

"Of course not," I said.

"Then we heard that Hungary was calling out the Honveds, but we still thought nothing of it."

"Certainly not," I said.

"And then we heard——"

"Yes, I know," I said, "you heard that Italy was calling out the Trombonari, and that Germany was calling in all the Landesgeschützshaft."

He looked at me.

"How did you know that?" he said.

"We heard it over here," I answered.

"Well," he went on, "next thing we knew we heard that the Russians were at Fryzzl."

"Great Heavens!" I exclaimed.

"Yes, at Fryzzl, not a hundred miles away. The very place we'd been at only two weeks before."

"Think of it!" I said. "If you'd been where you were two weeks after you were there, or if the Russians had been a hundred miles away from where they were, or even if Fryzzl had been a hundred miles nearer to Izzl——"

We both shuddered.

"It was a close call," said Parkins. "However, I said to Loo Jones, 'Loo, it's time to clear out.' And then, I tell you, our trouble began. First of all we couldn't get any money.

We went to the bank at Izzl and tried to get them to give us American dollars for Hungarian paper money; we had nothing else."

"And wouldn't they?"

"Absolutely refused. They said they hadn't any."

"By George," I exclaimed. "Isn't war dreadful? What on earth did you do?"

"Took a chance," said Parkins. "Went across to the railway station to buy our tickets with the Hungarian money."

"Did you get them?" I said.

"Yes," assented Parkins. "They said they'd sell us tickets. But they questioned us mighty closely; asked where we wanted to go to, what class we meant to travel by, how much luggage we had to register and so on. I tell you the fellow looked at us mighty closely."

"Were you in those clothes?" I asked.

"Yes," said Parkins, "but I guess he suspected we weren't Hungarians. You see, we couldn't either of us speak Hungarian. In fact we spoke nothing but English."

"That would give him a clue," I said.

"However," he went on, "he was civil enough in a way. We asked when was the next train to the sea coast, and he said there wasn't any."

"No trains?" I repeated.

"Not to the coast. The man said the reason was because there wasn't any railway to the coast. But he offered to sell us tickets to Vienna. We asked when the train would go and he said there wouldn't be one for two hours. So there we were waiting on that wretched little platform,—no place to sit down, no shade, unless one went into the waiting room itself,—for two mortal hours. And even then the train was an hour and a half late!"

"An hour and a half late!" I repeated.

"Yep!" said Parkins, "that's what things were like over there. So when we got on board the train we asked a man when it was due to get to Vienna, and he said he hadn't the faintest idea!"

"Good heavens!"

"Not the faintest idea. He told us to ask the conductor or one of the porters. No, sir,

I'll never forget that journey through to Vienna,—nine mortal hours! Nothing to eat, not a bite, except just in the middle of the day when they managed to hitch on a dining-car for a while. And they warned everybody that the dining-car was only on for an hour and a half. Commandeered, I guess after that," added Parkins, puffing his cigarette.

"Well," he continued, "we got to Vienna at last. I'll never forget the scene there, station full of people, trains coming and going, men, even women, buying tickets, big piles of luggage being shoved on trucks. It gave one a great idea of the reality of things."

"It must have," I said.

"Poor old Loo Jones was getting pretty well used up with it all. However, we determined to see it through somehow."

"What did you do next?"

"Tried again to get money: couldn't—they changed our Hungarian paper into Italian gold, but they refused to give us American money."

"Hoarding it?" I hinted.

"Exactly," said Parkins, "hoarding it all

for the war. Well anyhow we got on a train for Italy and there our troubles began all over again:—train stopped at the frontier,—officials (fellows in Italian uniforms) went all through it, opening hand baggage———"

"Not hand baggage!" I gasped.

"Yes, sir, even the hand baggage. Opened it all, or a lot of it anyway, and scribbled chalk marks over it. Yes, and worse than that,—I saw them take two fellows and sling them clear off the train,—they slung them right out on to the platform."

"What for?" I asked.

"Heaven knows," said Parkins,—"they said they had no tickets. In war time you know, when they're mobilizing, they won't let a soul ride on a train without a ticket."

"Infernal tyranny," I murmured.

"Isn't it? However, we got to Genoa at last, only to find that not a single one of our trunks had come with us!"

"Confiscated?" I asked.

"I don't know," said Parkins, "the head baggage man (he wears a uniform, you know, in

Italy just like a soldier) said it was because we'd forgotten to check them in Vienna. However there we were waiting for twenty-four hours with nothing but our valises."

"Right at the station?" I asked.

"No, at a hotel. We got the trunks later. They telegraphed to Vienna for them and managed to get them through somehow,—in a baggage car, I believe."

"And after that, I suppose, you had no more trouble."

"Trouble," said Parkins, "I should say we had. Couldn't get a steamer! They said there was none sailing out of Genoa for New York for three days! All cancelled, I guess, or else rigged up as cruisers."

"What on earth did you do?"

"Stuck it out as best we could: stayed right there in the hotel. Poor old Jones was pretty well collapsed! Couldn't do anything but sleep and eat, and sit on the piazza of the hotel."

"But you got your steamer at last?" I asked.

"Yes," he admitted, "we got it. But I never

99

want to go through another voyage like that
again, no sir!"

"What was wrong with it?" I asked, "bad
weather?"

"No, calm, but a peculiar calm, glassy, with
little ripples on the water,—uncanny sort of
feeling."

"What was wrong with the voyage?"

"Oh, just the feeling of it,—everything under strict rule you know—no lights anywhere
except just the electric lights,—smoking-room
closed tight at eleven o'clock,—decks all
washed down every night—officers up on the
bridge all day looking out over the sea,—no,
sir, I want no more of it. Poor old Loo Jones,
I guess he's quite used up: he can't speak of
it at all: just sits and broods, in fact I
doubt . . ."

.   .   .   .

At this moment Parkins's conversation was
interrupted by the entry of two newcomers into
the room. One of them had on a little Hungarian suit like the one Parkins wore, and was
talking loudly as they came in.

"Yes," he was saying, "we were caught there fair and square right in the war zone. We were at Izzl in the Carpathians, poor old Parkins and I——"

We looked round.

It was Loo Jones, describing his escape from Europe.

7.—The War Mania of Mr. Jinks and Mr. Blinks

THEY were sitting face to face at a lunch table at the club so near to me that I couldn't avoid hearing what they said. In any case they are both stout men with gurgling voices which carry.

"What Kitchener ought to do,"—Jinks was saying in a loud voice.

So I knew at once that he had the prevailing hallucination. He thought he was commanding armies in Europe.

After which I watched him show with three bits of bread and two olives and a dessert knife the way in which the German army could be destroyed.

Blinks looked at Jinks' diagram with a stern

impassive face, modelled on the Sunday supplement photogravures of Lord Kitchener.

"Your flank would be too much exposed," he said, pointing to Jinks' bread. He spoke with the hard taciturnity of a Joffre.

"My reserves cover it," said Jinks, moving two pepper pots to the support of the bread.

"Mind you," Jinks went on, "I don't say Kitchener *will* do this: I say this is what he *ought* to do: it's exactly the tactics of Kuropatkin outside of Mukden and it's precisely the same turning movement that Grant used before Richmond."

Blinks nodded gravely. Anybody who has seen the Grand Duke Nicholoevitch quietly accepting the advice of General Ruski under heavy artillery fire, will realize Blinks' manner to a nicety.

And, oddly enough, neither of them, I am certain, has ever had any larger ideas about the history of the Civil War than what can be got from reading *Uncle Tom's Cabin* and seeing Gillette play *Secret Service*. But this is part of the mania. Jinks and Blinks had suddenly developed the hallucination that they knew the history of all wars by a sort of instinct.

They rose soon after that, dusted off their waistcoats with their napkins and waddled heavily towards the door. I could hear them as they went talking eagerly of the need of keeping the troops in hard training. They were almost brutal in their severity. As they passed out of the door,—one at a time to avoid crowding,—they were still talking about it. Jinks was saying that our whole generation is overfed and soft. If he had his way he would take every man in the United States up to fortyseven years of age (Jinks is forty-eight) and train him to a shadow. Blinks went further. He said they should be trained hard up to fifty. He is fifty-one.

After that I used to notice Jinks and Blinks always together in the club, and always carrying on the European War.

I never knew which side they were on. They seemed to be on both. One day they commanded huge armies of Russians, and there was one week when Blinks and Jinks at the head of vast levies of Cossacks threatened to overrun the whole of Western Europe. It was dreadful to watch them burning churches and monasteries and to see Jinks throw whole convents full of white robed nuns into the flames like so much waste paper.

For a time I feared they would obliterate civilization itself. Then suddenly Blinks decided that Jinks' Cossacks were no good, not properly trained. He converted himself on the spot into a Prussian Field Marshal, declared himself organised to a pitch of organisation of which Jinks could form no idea, and swept Jinks' army off the earth, without using any men at all, by sheer organisation.

In this way they moved to and fro all winter over the map of Europe, carrying death and destruction everywhere and revelling in it.

But I think I liked best the wild excitement of their naval battles.

Jinks generally fancied himself a submarine and Blinks acted the part of a first-class battleship. Jinks would pop his periscope out of the water, take a look at Blinks merely for the fraction of a second, and then, like a flash, would dive under water again and start firing his torpedoes. He explained that he carried six.

But he was never quick enough for Blinks. One glimpse of his periscope miles and miles away was enough. Blinks landed him a contact shell in the side, sunk him with all hands, and then lined his yards with men and cheered. I have known Blinks sink Jinks at two miles, six miles—and once—in the club billiard room just after the battle of the Falkland Islands,— he got him fair and square at ten nautical miles.

Jinks of course claimed that he was not sunk. He had dived. He was two hundred feet under water quietly smiling at Blinks through his periscope. In fact the number of things that Jinks has learned to do through his periscope passes imagination.

Whenever I see him looking across at Blinks with his eyes half closed and with a baffling, quizzical expression in them, I know that he is looking at him through his periscope.

Now is the time for Blinks to watch out. If he relaxes his vigilance for a moment he'll be torpedoed as he sits, and sent flying, whiskey and soda and all, through the roof of the club, while Jinks dives into the basement.

Indeed it has come about of late, I don't know just how, that Jinks has more or less got command of the sea. A sort of tacit understanding has been reached that Blinks, whichever army he happens at the moment to command, is invincible on land. But Jinks, whether as a submarine or a battleship, controls the sea. No doubt this grew up in the natural evolution of their conversation. It makes things easier for both. Jinks even asks Blinks how many men there are in an army division, and what a sotnia of Cossacks is and what the Army Service Corps means. And Jinks in return has become a recognized expert in torpedoes and has taken to wearing a blue serge suit and referring to Lord Beresford as Charley.

But what I noticed chiefly about the war mania of Jinks and Blinks was their splendid indifference to slaughter. They had gone into the war with a grim resolution to fight it out to a finish. If Blinks thought to terrify Jinks by threatening to burn London, he little knew his man. "All right," said Jinks, taking a fresh light for his cigar, "burn it! By doing so, you destroy, let us say, two million of my women and children? Very good. Am I injured by that? No. You merely stimulate me to recruiting."

There was something awful in the grimness of the struggle as carried on by Blinks and Jinks.

The rights of neutrals and non-combatants, Red Cross nurses, and regimental clergymen they laughed to scorn. As for moving-picture men and newspaper correspondents, Jinks and Blinks hanged them on every tree in Belgium and Poland.

With combatants in this frame of mind the war I suppose might have lasted forever.

But it came to an end accidentally,—fortuitously, as all great wars are apt to. And by accident also, I happened to see the end of it.

It was late one evening. Jinks and Blinks were coming down the steps of the club, and as they came they were speaking with some vehemence on their favourite topic.

"I tell you," Jinks was saying, "war is a great thing. We needed it, Blinks. We were all getting too soft, too scared of suffering and pain. We wilt at a bayonet charge, we shudder at the thought of wounds. Bah!" he continued, "what does it matter if a few hundred thousands of human beings are cut to pieces. We need to get back again to the old Viking standard, the old pagan ideas of suffering——"

And as he spoke he got it.

The steps of the club were slippery with the evening's rain,—not so slippery as the frozen lakes of East Prussia or the hills where Jinks and Blinks had been campaigning all winter, but slippery enough for a stout man whose nation has neglected his training. As Jinks waved his stick in the air to illustrate the glory of a bayonet charge, he slipped and fell sideways on the stone steps. His shin bone smacked against the edge of the stone in a way that was pretty well up to the old Viking standard of such things. Blinks with the shock of the collision fell also,—backwards on the top step, his head striking first. He lay, to all appearance, as dead as the most insignificant casualty in Servia.

I watched the waiters carrying them into the club, with that new field ambulance attitude towards pain which is getting so popular. They had evidently acquired precisely the old pagan attitude that Blinks and Jinks desired.

And the evening after that I saw Blinks and Jinks, both more or less bandaged, sitting in a corner of the club beneath a rubber tree, making peace.

Jinks was moving out of Montenegro and Blinks was foregoing all claims to Polish Prussia; Jinks was offering Alsace-Lorraine to Blinks, and Blinks in a fit of chivalrous enthusiasm was refusing to take it. They were disbanding troops, blowing up fortresses, sinking their warships and offering indemnities which they both refused to take. Then as they talked, Jinks leaned forward and said something to

Blinks in a low voice,—a final proposal of terms evidently.

Blinks nodded, and Jinks turned and beckoned to a waiter, with the words,—

"One Scotch whiskey and soda, and one stein of Würtemburger Bier——"

And when I heard this, I knew that the war was over.

8.—*The Ground Floor*

I HADN'T seen Ellesworth since our college days, twenty years before, at the time when he used to borrow two dollars and a half from the professor of Public Finance to tide him over the week end.

Then quite suddenly he turned up at the club one day and had afternoon tea with me.

His big clean shaven face had lost nothing of its impressiveness, and his spectacles had the same glittering magnetism as in the days when he used to get the college bursar to accept his note of hand for his fees.

And he was still talking European politics just as he used to in the days of our earlier acquaintance.

"Mark my words," he said across the little tea-table, with one of the most piercing glances I have ever seen, "the whole Balkan situation was only a beginning. We are on the eve of a great pan-Slavonic upheaval." And then he added, in a very quiet, casual tone: "By the way, could you let me have twenty-five dollars till to-morrow?"

"A pan-Slavonic movement!" I ejaculated. "Do you really think it possible? No, I couldn't."

"You must remember," Ellesworth went on, "Russia means to reach out and take all she can get;" and he added, "how about fifteen till Friday?"

"She may reach for it," I said, "but I doubt if she'll get anything. I'm sorry. I haven't got it."

"You're forgetting the Bulgarian element," he continued, his animation just as eager as before. "The Slavs never forget what they owe to one another."

Here Ellesworth drank a sip of tea and then said quietly, "Could you make it ten till Saturday at twelve?"

I looked at him more closely. I noticed now his frayed cuffs and the dinginess of his over-brushed clothes. Not even the magnetism of his spectacles could conceal it. Perhaps I had been forgetting something, whether the Bulgarian element or not.

I compromised at ten dollars till Saturday.

"The Slav," said Ellesworth, as he pocketed the money, "is peculiar. He never forgets."

"What are you doing now?" I asked him. "Are you still in insurance?" I had a vague recollection of him as employed in that business.

"No," he answered. "I gave it up. I didn't like the outlook. It was too narrow. The atmosphere cramped me. I want," he said, "a bigger horizon."

"Quite so," I answered quietly. I had known men before who had lost their jobs. It is generally the cramping of the atmosphere that does it. Some of them can use up a tremendous lot of horizon.

"At present," Ellesworth went on, "I am in finance. I'm promoting companies."

"Oh, yes," I said. I had seen companies promoted before.

"Just now," continued Ellesworth, "I'm

114

working on a thing that I think will be rather
a big thing. I shouldn't want it talked about
outside, but it's a matter of taking hold of the
cod fisheries of the Grand Banks,—practically
amalgamating them—and perhaps combining
with them the entire herring output, and the
whole of the sardine catch of the Mediterra-
nean. If it goes through," he added, "I shall
be in a position to let you in on the ground
floor."

I knew the ground floor of old. I have already many friends sitting on it; and others
who have fallen through it into the basement.

I said, "thank you," and he left me.

"That was Ellesworth, wasn't it?" said a
friend of mine who was near me. "Poor devil.
I knew him slightly,—always full of some new
and wild idea of making money. He was talking to me the other day of the possibility of
cornering all the huckleberry crop and making
refined sugar. Isn't it amazing what fool ideas
fellows like him are always putting up to business men?"

We both laughed.

After that I didn't see Ellesworth for some weeks.

Then I met him in the club again. How he paid his fees there I do not know.

This time he was seated among a litter of foreign newspapers with a cup of tea and a ten-cent package of cigarettes beside him.

"Have one of these cigarettes," he said. "I get them specially. They are milder than what we have in the club here."

They certainly were.

"Note what I say," Ellesworth went on. "The French Republic is going to gain from now on a stability that it never had." He seemed greatly excited about it. But his voice changed to a quiet tone as he added, "Could you, without inconvenience, let me have five dollars?"

So I knew that the cod-fish and the sardines were still unamalgamated.

"What about the fisheries thing?" I asked. "Did it go through?"

"The fisheries? No, I gave it up. I refused to go forward with it. The New York people concerned were too shy, too timid to tackle it. I finally had to put it to them very straight that they must either stop shilly-shally-ing and declare themselves, or the whole business was off."

"Did they declare themselves?" I questioned.

"They did," said Ellesworth, "but I don't regret it. I'm working now on a much bigger thing,—something with greater possibilities in it. When the right moment comes I'll let you in on the ground floor."

I thanked him and we parted.

The next time I saw Ellesworth he told me at once that he regarded Albania as unable to stand by itself. So I gave him five dollars on the spot and left him.

A few days after that he called me up on the telephone to tell me that the whole of Asia Minor would have to be redistributed. The redistribution cost me five dollars more.

Then I met him on the street, and he said that Persia was disintegrating, and took from me a dollar and a half.

When I passed him next in the street he was very busy amalgamating Chinese tramways. It appeared that there was a ground floor in China, but I kept off it.

Each time I saw Ellesworth he looked a little shabbier than the last. Then one day he called me up on the telephone, and made an appointment.

His manner when I joined him was full of importance.

"I want you at once," he said in a commanding tone, "to write me your cheque for a hundred dollars."

"What's the matter?" I asked.

"I am now able," said Ellesworth, "to put you in on the ground floor of one of the biggest things in years."

"Thanks," I said, "the ground floor is no place for me."

"Don't misunderstand me," said Ellesworth. "This is a big thing. It's an idea I've been working on for some time,—making refined sugar from the huckleberry crop. It's a certainty. I can get you shares now at five dollars. They'll go to five hundred when we put them on the market,—and I can run you in for a block of stock for promotion services as well. All you have to do is to give me right now a hundred dollars,—cash or your cheque,—and I can arrange the whole thing for you."

I smiled.

"My dear Ellesworth," I said, "I hope you won't mind if I give you a little bit of good advice. Why not drop all this idea of quick money? There's nothing in it. The business world has grown too shrewd for it. Take an ordinary decent job and stick to it. Let me use my influence," I added, "to try and get you into something with a steady salary, and with your brains you're bound to get on in time."

Ellesworth looked pained. A "steady job" sounded to him like a "ground floor" to me.

After that I saw nothing of him for weeks. But I didn't forget him. I looked about and secured for him a job as a canvassing agent for a book firm at a salary of five dollars a week, and a commission of one-tenth of one per cent.

I was waiting to tell him of his good luck, when I chanced to see him at the club again.

But he looked transformed.

He had on a long frock coat that reached nearly to his knees. He was leading a little procession of very heavy men in morning coats, upstairs towards the private luncheon rooms. They moved like a funeral, puffing as they went. I had seen company directors before and I knew what they were at sight.

"It's a small club and rather inconvenient," Ellesworth was saying, "and the horizon of some of its members rather narrow," here he nodded to me as he passed,—"but I can give you a fairly decent lunch."

I watched them as they disappeared upstairs.

"That's Ellesworth, isn't it?" said a man near me. It was the same man who had asked about him before.

"Yes," I answered.

"Giving a lunch to his directors, I suppose," said my friend; "lucky dog."

"His directors?" I asked.

"Yes, hadn't you heard? He's just cleaned

up half a million or more,—some new scheme for making refined sugar out of huckleberries. Isn't it amazing what shrewd ideas these big business men get hold of? They say they're unloading the stock at five hundred dollars. It only cost them about five to organize. If only one could get on to one of these things early enough, eh?"

I assented sadly.

And the next time I am offered a chance on the ground floor I am going to take it, even if it's only the barley floor of a brewery.

It appears that there is such a place after all.

9.—*The Hallucination of Mr. Butt*

IT is the hallucination of Mr. Butt's life that he lives to do good. At whatever cost of time or trouble to himself, he does it. Whether people appear to desire it or not, he insists on helping them along.

His time, his company and his advice are at the service not only of those who seek them but of those who, in the mere appearances of things, are not asking for them.

You may see the beaming face of Mr. Butt appear at the door of all those of his friends who are stricken with the minor troubles of life. Whenever Mr. Butt learns that any of his friends are moving house, buying furniture, selling furniture, looking for a maid, dismissing a maid, seeking a chauffeur, suing a plumber or buying a piano,—he is at their side in a moment.

So when I met him one night in the cloak room of the club putting on his raincoat and his galoshes with a peculiar beaming look on his face, I knew that he was up to some sort of benevolence.

"Come upstairs," I said, "and play billiards." I saw from his general appearance that it was a perfectly safe offer.

"My dear fellow," said Mr. Butt, "I only wish I could. I wish I had the time. I am sure it would cheer you up immensely if I could. But I'm just going out."

"Where are you off to?" I asked, for I knew he wanted me to say it.

"I'm going out to see the Everleigh-Joneses, —you know them? no?—just come to the city, you know, moving into their new house, out on Seldom Avenue."

"But," I said, "that's away out in the sub-urbs, is it not, a mile or so beyond the car tracks?"

"Something like that," answered Mr. Butt.

"And it's going on for ten o'clock and it's starting to rain——"

"Pooh, pooh," said Mr. Butt, cheerfully, adjusting his galoshes. "I never mind the rain, —does one good. As to their house. I've not been there yet but I can easily find it. I've a very simple system for finding a house at night by merely knocking at the doors in the neighborhood till I get it."

"Isn't it rather late to go there?" I protested.

"My dear fellow," said Mr. Butt warmly, "I don't mind that a bit. The way I look at it is, here are these two young people, only married a few weeks, just moving into their new house, everything probably upside down, no one there but themselves, no one to cheer them up,"—he was wriggling into his raincoat as he spoke and working himself into a frenzy of benevolence,—"good gracious, I only learned at dinner time that they had come to town, or I'd have been out there days ago,—days ago——"

And with that Mr. Butt went bursting forth into the rain, his face shining with good will under the street lamps.

The next day I saw him again at the club at lunch time.

"Well," I asked, "did you find the Joneses?"

"I did," said Mr. Butt, "and by George I was glad that I'd gone—quite a lot of trouble to find the house (though I didn't mind that; I expected it)—had to knock at twenty houses at least to get it,—very dark and wet out there, —no street lights yet,—however I simply pounded at the doors until some one showed a light—at every house I called out the same things, 'Do you know where the Everleigh Joneses live?' They didn't. 'All right,' I said, 'go back to bed. Don't bother to come down.'

"But I got to the right spot at last. I found the house all dark. Jones put his head out of an upper window. 'Hullo,' I called out; 'it's Butt.' 'I'm awfully sorry,' he said, 'we've gone to bed.' 'My dear boy,' I called back, 'don't apologize at all. Throw me down the key and I'll wait while you dress. I don't mind a bit.'

"Just think of it," continued Mr. Butt, "those two poor souls going to bed at half past ten, through sheer dullness! By George, I was glad I'd come. 'Now then,' I said to myself, 'let's cheer them up a little, let's make things a little brighter here.'

"Well, down they came and we sat there on furniture cases and things and had a chat. Mrs. Jones wanted to make me some coffee. 'My dear girl,' I said (I knew them both when they were children) 'I absolutely refuse. Let *me* make it.' They protested. I insisted. I went at it,—kitchen all upset—had to open at least twenty tins to get the coffee. However, I made it at last. 'Now,' I said, 'drink it.' They said they had some an hour or so ago. 'Nonsense,' I said, 'drink it.' Well, we sat and chatted away till midnight. They were dull at first and I had to do all the talking. But I set myself to it. I can talk, you know, when I try. Presently about midnight they seemed to brighten up a little. Jones looked at his watch. 'By Jove,' he said, in an animated way, 'it's after midnight.' I think he was pleased at the way the evening was going; after that we chatted away more comfortably. Every little

126

while Jones would say, 'By Jove, it's half past twelve,' or 'it's one o'clock,' and so on.

"I took care, of course, not to stay too late. But when I left them I promised that I'd come back to-day to help straighten things up. They protested, but I insisted."

That same day Mr. Butt went out to the suburbs and put the Joneses' furniture to rights.

"I worked all afternoon," he told me afterwards,—"hard at it with my coat off—got the pictures up first—they'd been trying to put them up by themselves in the morning. I had to take down every one of them—not a single one right,—'Down they come,' I said, and went at it with a will."

A few days later Mr. Butt gave me a further report. "Yes," he said, "the furniture is all unpacked and straightened out but I don't like it. There's a lot of it I don't quite like. I half feel like advising Jones to sell it and get some more. But I don't want to do that till I'm quite certain about it."

After that Mr. Butt seemed much occupied and I didn't see him at the club for some time.

"How about the Everleigh-Joneses?" I asked. "Are they comfortable in their new house?"

Mr. Butt shook his head. "It won't do," he said. "I was afraid of it from the first. I'm moving Jones in nearer to town. I've been out all morning looking for an apartment; when I get the right one I shall move him. I like an apartment far better than a house."

So the Joneses in due course of time were moved. After that Mr. Butt was very busy selecting a piano, and advising them on wall paper and woodwork.

They were hardly settled in their new home when fresh trouble came to them.

"Have you heard about Everleigh-Jones?" said Mr. Butt one day with an anxious face.

"No," I answered.

"He's ill—some sort of fever—poor chap—been ill three days, and they never told me or sent for me—just like their grit—meant to fight it out alone. I'm going out there at once."

From day to day I had reports from Mr. Butt of the progress of Jones's illness.

"I sit with him every day," he said. "Poor chap,—he was very bad yesterday for a while, —mind wandered—quite delirious—I could hear him from the next room—seemed to think some one was hunting him—'Is that damn old fool gone,' I heard him say.

"I went in and soothed him. 'There is no one here, my dear boy,' I said, 'no one, only Butt.' He turned over and groaned. Mrs. Jones begged me to leave him. 'You look quite used up,' she said. 'Go out into the open air.' 'My dear Mrs. Jones,' I said, 'what *does* it matter about me?'"

Eventually, thanks no doubt to Mr. Butt's assiduous care, Everleigh-Jones got well.

"Yes," said Mr. Butt to me a few weeks later, "Jones is all right again now, but his illness has been a long hard pull. I haven't had an evening to myself since it began. But I'm paid, sir, now, more than paid for anything I've done,—the gratitude of those two people

—it's unbelievable—you ought to see it. Why do you know that dear little woman is so worried for fear that my strength has been overtaxed that she wants me to take a complete rest and go on a long trip somewhere—suggested first that I should go south. 'My dear Mrs. Jones,' I said laughing, 'that's the *one* place I will not go. Heat is the one thing I *can't* stand.' She wasn't nonplussed for a moment. 'Then go north,' she said. 'Go up to Canada, or better still go to Labrador,'—and in a minute that kind little woman was hunting up railway maps to see how far north I could get by rail. 'After that,' she said, 'you can go on snowshoes.' She's found that there's a steamer to Ungava every spring and she wants me to run up there on one steamer and come back on the next."

"It must be very gratifying," I said.

"Oh, it is, it is," said Mr. Butt warmly. "It's well worth anything I do. It more than repays me. I'm alone in the world and my friends are all I have. I can't tell you how it goes to my heart when I think of all my friends, here in the club and in the town, always glad to see me, always protesting against my little kindnesses and yet never quite satisfied about anything unless they can get my advice and hear what I have to say.

"Take Jones for instance," he continued— "do you know, really now as a fact,—the hall porter assures me of it,—every time Everleigh-Jones enters the club here the first thing he does is to sing out, 'Is Mr. Butt in the club?' It warms me to think of it." Mr. Butt paused, one would have said there were tears in his eyes. But if so the kindly beam of his spectacles shone through them like the sun through April rain. He left me and passed into the cloak room.

He had just left the hall when a stranger entered, a narrow, meek man with a hunted face. He came in with a furtive step and looked about him apprehensively.

"Is Mr. Butt in the club?" he whispered to the hall porter.

"Yes, sir, he's just gone into the cloak room, sir, shall I——"

But the man had turned and made a dive for the front door and had vanished.

"Who is that?" I asked.

"That's a new member, sir, Mr. Everleigh-Jones," said the hall porter.

RAM SPUDD THE
NEW WORLD SINGER

IV.—Ram Spudd The New World Singer. Is He Divinely Inspired? Or Is He Not? At Any Rate We Discovered Him.*

THE discovery of a new poet is always a joy to the cultivated world. It is therefore with the greatest pleasure that we are able to announce that we ourselves, acting quite independently and without aid from any of the English reviews of the day, have discovered one. In the person of Mr. Ram Spudd, of whose work we give specimens below, we feel that we reveal to our readers a genius of the first order. Unlike one of the most recently

* Mr. Spudd was discovered by the author for the New York *Life*. He is already recognized as superior to Tennyson and second only, as a writer of imagination, to the Sultan of Turkey.

discovered English poets who is a Bengalee, and another who is a full-blooded Yak, Mr. Spudd is, we believe, a Navajo Indian. We believe this from the character of his verse. Mr. Spudd himself we have not seen. But when he forwarded his poems to our office and offered with characteristic modesty to sell us his entire works for seventy-five cents, we felt in closing with his offer that we were dealing not only with a poet, but with one of nature's gentlemen.

Mr. Spudd, we understand, has had no education. Other newly discovered poets have had, apparently, some. Mr. Spudd has had, evidently, none. We lay stress on this point. Without it we claim it is impossible to understand his work.

What we particularly like about Ram Spudd, and we do not say this because we discovered him but because we believe it and must say it, is that he belongs not to one school but to all of them. As a nature poet we doubt very much if he has his equal; as a psychologist, we are sure he has not. As a clear lucid thinker he is undoubtedly in the first rank; while as a mystic he is a long way in front of it. The specimens of Mr. Spudd's verse which we append herewith were selected, we are happy to assure our readers, purely at random from his work. We first blindfolded ourselves and then, standing with our feet in warm water and having one hand tied behind our back, we groped among the papers on our desk before us and selected for our purpose whatever specimens first came to hand.

As we have said, or did we say it, it is perhaps as a nature poet that Ram Spudd excels. Others of our modern school have carried the observation of natural objects to a high degree of very nice precision, but with Mr. Spudd the observation of nature becomes an almost scientific process. Nothing escapes him. The green of the grass he detects as in an instant. The sky is no sooner blue than he remarks it with unerring certainty. Every bird note, every bee call, is familiar to his trained ear. Perhaps we cannot do better than quote the opening lines of a singularly beautiful sample of Ram Spudd's genius which seems to us the last word in nature poetry.   It is called, with characteristic daintiness—

SPRING THAW IN THE AHUNTSIC WOODS, NEAR PASPEBIAC, PASSAMOQUODDY COUNTY

'(We would like to say that, to our ears at least, there is a music in this title like the sound of falling water, or of chopped ice.   But we must not interrupt ourselves.   We now begin. Listen.)

The thermometer is standing this morning at thirty-three decimal one.
As a consequence it is freezing in the shade, but it is thawing in the sun.
There is a certain amount of snow on the ground, but of course not too much.
The air is what you would call humid, but not disagreeable to the touch.
Where I am standing I find myself practically surrounded by trees,
It is simply astonishing the number of the different varieties one sees.
I've grown so wise I can tell each different tree by seeing it glisten,

138

But if that test fails I simply put my ear to the tree
    and listen,
And, well, I suppose it is only a silly fancy of mine
    perhaps,
But do you know I'm getting to tell different trees
    by the sound of their saps.
After I have noticed all the trees, and named those I
    know in words,
I stand quite still and look all round to see if there
    are any birds,
And yesterday, close where I was standing, sitting in
    some brush on the snow,
I saw what I was practically absolutely certain was an
    early crow.
I sneaked up ever so close and was nearly beside it,
    when say!
It turned and took one look at me, and flew away.

But we should not wish our readers to think that Ram Spudd is always and only the contemplative poet of the softer aspects of nature. Oh, by no means. There are times when waves of passion sweep over him in such prodigious volume as to roll him to and fro like a pebble in the surf. Gusts of emotion blow over him with such violence as to hurl him pro and con with inconceivable fury. In such moods, if it were not for the relief offered by writing verse we really do not know what would happen to him. His verse written under the impulse of such emotions marks him as one of the greatest masters of passion, wild and yet restrained, objectionable and yet printable, that have appeared on this side of the Atlantic. We append herewith a portion, or half portion, of his little gem entitled

YOU

You!
With your warm, full, rich, red, ripe lips,
And your beautifully manicured finger-tips!
You!
With your heaving, panting, rapidly expanding and
    contracting chest,
Lying against my perfectly ordinary shirt-front and
    dinner-jacket vest.
It is too much
Your touch
As such.
It and
Your hand,
Can you not understand?
Last night an ostrich feather from your fragrant hair
    Unnoticed fell.
I guard it

Well.
Yestere'en
From your tiara I have slid,
    Unseen,
    A single diamond,
    And I keep it
    Hid.
Last night you left inside the vestibule upon the sill
    A quarter dollar,
    And I have it
    Still.

But even those who know Ram Spudd as the poet of nature or of passion still only know a part of his genius. Some of his highest flights rise from an entirely different inspiration, and deal with the public affairs of the nation. They are in every sense comparable to the best work of the poets laureate of England dealing with similar themes. As soon as we had seen Ram Spudd's work of this kind, we cried, that is we said to our stenographer, "What a pity that in this republic we have no laureateship. Here is a man who might truly fill it." Of the poem of this kind we should wish to quote, if our limits of space did not prevent it, Mr. Spudd's exquisite

ODE ON THE REDUCTION OF THE
UNITED STATES TARIFF

It is a matter of the very gravest concern to at least
nine-tenths of the business interests in the
United States,
Whether an all-round reduction of the present tariff
either on an ad valorem or a specific basis
Could be effected without a serious disturbance of the
general industrial situation of the country.

But, no, we must not quote any more. No we
really mustn't. Yet we cannot refrain from
inserting a reference to the latest of these laureate poems of Ram Spudd. It appears to us to
be a matchless specimen of its class, and to
settle once and for all the vexed question
(though we ourselves never vexed it) of
whether true poetry can deal with national occasions as they arise. It is entitled:

THE BANKER'S EUTHANASIA: OR,
THE FEDERAL RESERVE CURRENCY
ACT OF 1914,

and, though we do not propose to reproduce it
here, our distinct feeling is that it will take its

rank beside Mr. Spudd's *Elegy on the Inter-state Commerce Act*, and his *Thoughts on the Proposal of a Uniform Pure Food Law*.

But our space does not allow us to present Ram Spudd in what is after all his greatest aspect, that of a profound psychologist, a questioner of the very meaning of life itself. His poem *Death and Gloom*, from which we must refrain from quoting at large, contains such striking passages as the following:

> Why do I breathe, or do I?
> What am I for, and whither do I go?
> What skills it if I live, and if I die,
> What boots it?

Any one knowing Ram Spudd as we do will realize that these questions, especially the last, are practically unanswerable.

ARISTOCRATIC
ANECDOTES

V.—Aristocratic Anecdotes or Little Stories of Great People

I HAVE been much struck lately by the many excellent little anecdotes of celebrated people that have appeared in recent memoirs and found their way thence into the columns of the daily press. There is something about them so deliciously pointed, their humour is so exquisite, that I think we ought to have more of them. To this end I am trying to circulate on my own account a few anecdotes which seem somehow to have been overlooked.

Here, for example, is an excellent thing which comes, if I remember rightly, from the vivacious Memoir of Lady Ranelagh de Chit Chat.

ANECDOTE OF THE DUKE OF STRATHYTHAN

Lady Ranelagh writes: "The Duke of Strathythan (I am writing of course of the seventeenth Duke, not of his present Grace) was, as everybody knows, famous for his hospitality. It was not perhaps generally known that the Duke was as witty as he was hospitable. I recall a most amusing incident that happened the last time but two that I was staying at Strathythan Towers. As we sat down to lunch (we were a very small and intimate party, there being only forty-three of us) the Duke, who was at the head of the table, looked up from the roast of beef that he was carving, and running his eye about the guests was heard to murmur, 'I'm afraid there isn't enough beef to go round.'

"There was nothing to do, of course, but to roar with laughter and the incident passed off with perfect *savoir faire*."

Here is another story which I think has not had all the publicity that it ought to. I found it in the book *Shot, Shell and Shrapnell or Sixty Years as a War Correspondent*, recently written by Mr. Maxim Gatling whose exploits are familiar to all readers.

ANECDOTE OF LORD KITCHENER

"I was standing," writes Mr. Maxim, "immediately between Lord Kitchener and Lord Wolsley (with Lord Roberts a little to the rear of us), and we were laughing and chatting as we always did when the enemy were about to open fire on us. Suddenly we found ourselves the object of the most terrific hail of bullets. For a few moments the air was black with them. As they went past I could not refrain from exchanging a quiet smile with Lord Kitchener, and another with Lord Wolsley. Indeed I have never, except perhaps on twenty or thirty occasions, found myself exposed to such an awful fusillade.

"Kitchener, who habitually uses an eye-glass (among his friends), watched the bullets go singing by, and then, with that inimitable *sangfroid* which he reserves for his intimates, said,

" 'I'm afraid if we stay here we may get hit.'

"We all moved away laughing heartily.

"To add to the joke, Lord Roberts' aide-de-camp was shot in the pit of the stomach as we went."

The next anecdote which I reproduce may be already too well known to my readers. The career of Baron Snorch filled so large a page in the history of European diplomacy that the publication of his recent memoirs was awaited

with profound interest by half the chancelleries
of Europe. (Even the other half were half
excited over them.) The tangled skein in
which the politics of Europe are enveloped was
perhaps never better illustrated than in this
fascinating volume. Even at the risk of re-
peating what is already familiar, I offer the
following for what it is worth—or even less.

NEW LIGHT ON THE LIFE OF CAVOUR

"I have always regarded Count Cavour," writes the
Baron, "as one of the most impenetrable diplomatists
whom it has been my lot to meet. I distinctly recall
an incident in connection with the famous Congress
of Paris of 1856 which rises before my mind as
vividly as if it were yesterday. I was seated in one
of the large salons of the Elysée Palace (I often
used to sit there) playing vingt-et-un together with
Count Cavour, the Duc de Magenta, the Marquese
di Casa Mombasa, the Conte di Piccolo Pochito and
others whose names I do not recollect. The stakes had
been, as usual, very high, and there was a large pile
of gold on the table. No one of us, however, paid any
attention to it, so absorbed were we all in the thought
of the momentous crises that were impending. At in-
tervals the Emperor Napoleon III passed in and out of
the room, and paused to say a word or two, with

well-feigned *éloignement,* to the players, who replied
with such *dégagement* as they could.

"While the play was at its height a servant appeared with a telegram on a silver tray. He handed
it to Count Cavour. The Count paused in his play,
opened the telegram, read it and then with the most
inconceivable nonchalance, put it in his pocket. We
stared at him in amazement for a moment, and then
the Duc, with the infinite ease of a trained diplomat,
quietly resumed his play.

"Two days afterward, meeting Count Cavour at a
reception of the Empress Eugénie, I was able, un-
observed, to whisper in his ear, 'What was in the telegram?' 'Nothing of any consequence,' he answered.
From that day to this I have never known what it
contained. My readers," concludes Baron Snorch,
"may believe this or not as they like, but I give them
my word that it is true.

"Probably they will not believe it."

I cannot resist appending to these anecdotes
a charming little story from that well-known
book, *Sorrows of a Queen.* The writer, Lady
de Weary, was an English gentlewoman who
was for many years Mistress of the Robes at
one of the best known German courts. Her af-
fection for her royal mistress is evident on
every page of her memoirs.

TENDERNESS OF A QUEEN

Lady de W. writes:

"My dear mistress, the late Queen of Saxe-Covia-Slitz-in-Mein, was of a most tender and sympathetic disposition. The goodness of her heart broke forth on all occasions. I well remember how one day, on seeing a cabman in the Poodel Platz kicking his horse in the stomach, she stopped in her walk and said, 'Oh, poor horse! if he goes on kicking it like that he'll hurt it.' "

I may say in conclusion that I think if people would only take a little more pains to resuscitate anecdotes of this sort, there might be a lot more of them found.

EDUCATION MADE AGREEABLE

VI.—*Education Made Agreeable or the Diversions of a Professor*

A FEW days ago during a pause in one of my college lectures (my class being asleep) I sat reading Draper's *Intellectual Development of Europe.* Quite suddenly I came upon the following sentence:

"Eratosthenes cast everything he wished to teach into poetry. By this means he made it attractive, and he was able to spread his system all over Asia Minor."

This came to me with a shock of an intellectual discovery. I saw at once how I could spread my system, or parts of it, all over the United States and Canada. To make education attractive! There it is! To call in the help of poetry, of music, of grand opera, if need be, to aid in the teaching of the dry subjects of the college class room.

I set to work at once on the project and already I have enough results to revolutionize education.

In the first place I have compounded a blend of modern poetry and mathematics, which retains all the romance of the latter and loses none of the dry accuracy of the former. Here is an example:

The poem of

LORD ULLIN'S DAUGHTER

expressed as

A PROBLEM IN TRIGONOMETRY

Introduction. A party of three persons, a Scotch nobleman, a young lady and an elderly boatman stand on the banks of a river (R), which, for private reasons, they desire to cross. Their only means of transport is a boat, of which the boatman, if squared, is able to row at a rate proportional to the square of the distance. The boat, however, has a leak (S), through which a quantity of water passes sufficient to sink it after traversing an indeterminate distance (D). Given the square of the boatman and the mean situation of all concerned, to find whether the boat will pass the river safely or sink.

156

A chieftain to the Highlands bound
   Cried "Boatman do not tarry!
And I'll give you a silver pound
   To row me o'er the ferry."
Before them raged the angry tide
$X^2 + Y$ from side to side.

Outspake the hardy Highland wight,
   "I'll go, my chief, I'm ready;
It is not for your silver bright,
   But for your winsome lady."
And yet he seemed to manifest
   A certain hesitation;
His head was sunk upon his breast
   In puzzled calculation.

"Suppose the river $X + Y$
And call the distance Q
Then dare we thus the gods defy
I think we dare, don't you?
   Our floating power expressed in words
   Is $\dfrac{X + 47}{3}$"

"Oh, haste thee, haste," the lady cries,
"Though tempests round us gather
I'll face the raging of the skies
But please cut out the Algebra."

The boat has left the stormy shore (S)
A stormy C before her
$C_1 \ C_2 \ C_3 \ C_4$
The tempest gathers o'er her
   The thunder rolls, the lightning smites 'em
   And the rain falls ad infinitum.

In vain the aged boatman strains,
His heaving sides reveal his pains;
The angry water gains apace
Both of his sides and half his base,
   Till, as he sits, he seems to lose
   The square of his hypotenuse.

The boat advanced to $X + 2$,
Lord Ullin reached the fixed point Q,—
   Then the boat sank from human eye,
OY, OY^2, OGY.

But this is only a sample of what can be
done. I have realised that all our technical
books are written and presented in too dry a
fashion. They don't make the most of themselves. Very often the situation implied is in-
tensely sensational, and if set out after the
fashion of an up-to-date newspaper, would be
wonderfully effective.

Here, for example, you have Euclid writing

in a perfectly prosaic way all in small type such an item as the following:

"A perpendicular is let fall on a line BC so as to bisect it at the point C etc., etc.," just as if it were the most ordinary occurrence in the world. Every newspaper man will see at once that it ought to be set up thus:

AWFUL CATASTROPHE
PERPENDICULAR FALLS HEADLONG
ON A GIVEN POINT
The Line at C said to be completely bisected
President of the Line makes Statement
etc., etc., etc.

But I am not contenting myself with merely describing my system. I am putting it to the test. I am preparing a new and very special edition of my friend Professor Daniel Murray's work on the Calculus. This is a book little known to the general public. I suppose one may say without exaggeration that outside of the class room it is hardly read at all.

Yet I venture to say that when my new edition is out it will be found on the tables of every cultivated home, and will be among the best sellers of the year. All that is needed is to give to this really monumental book the same chance that is given to every other work of fiction in the modern market.

First of all I wrap it in what is called technically a jacket. This is of white enamelled paper, and on it is a picture of a girl, a very pretty girl, in a summer dress and sunbonnet sitting swinging on a bough of a cherry tree. Across the cover in big black letters are the words:

THE CALCULUS

and beneath them the legend "the most daring book of the day." This, you will observe, is perfectly true. The reviewers of the mathematical journals when this book first came out agreed that "Professor Murray's views on the Calculus were the most daring yet published." They said, too, that they hoped that the professor's unsound theories of infinitesimal rectitude would not remain unchallenged. Yet the public somehow missed it all, and one of the most profitable scandals in the publishing trade was missed for the lack of a little business enterprise.

My new edition will give this book its first real chance.

I admit that the inside has to be altered,—but not very much. The real basis of interest is there. The theories in the book are just as interesting as those raised in the modern novel. All that is needed is to adopt the device, familiar in novels, of clothing the theories in personal form and putting the propositions advanced into the mouths of the characters, instead of leaving them as unsupported statements of the author. Take for example Dr. Murray's beginning. It is very good,—any one will admit it,—fascinatingly clever, but it lacks heart.

It runs:

If two magnitudes, one of which is determined by a straight line and the other by a parabola approach one another, the rectangle included by the revolution of each will be equal to the sum of a series of indeterminate rectangles.

Now this is,—quite frankly,—dull. The situation is there; the idea is good, and, whether one agrees or not, is at least as brilliantly original as even the best of our recent novels. But I find it necessary to alter the presentation of the plot a little bit. As I re-edit it the opening of the Calculus runs thus:

On a bright morning in June along a path gay with the opening efflorescence of the hibiscus and entangled here and there with the wild blossoms of the convolvulus,—two magnitudes might have been seen approaching one another. The one magnitude who held a tennis-racket in his hand, carried himself with a beautiful erectness and moved with a firmness such as would have led Professor Murray to exclaim in despair— Let it be granted that A. B. (for such was our hero's name) is a straight line. The other magnitude, which drew near with a step at once elusive and fascinating, revealed as she walked a figure so exquisite in its every curve as to call from her geometrical acquaintances the ecstatic exclamation, "Let it be granted that M is a parabola."

The beautiful magnitude of whom we have last spoken, bore on her arm as she walked, a tiny dog over which her fair head was bent in endearing caresses; indeed such was her attention to the dog *Vi* (his full name was Velocity but he was called Vi for short) that her wayward footsteps carried her not in a straight line but in a direction so constantly changing as to lead that acute observer, Professor Murray, to the conclusion that her path could only be described by the amount of attraction ascribable to Vi.

Guided thus along their respective paths, the two magnitudes presently met with such suddenness that they almost intersected.

"I beg your pardon," said the first magnitude very rigidly.

"You ought to indeed," said the second rather sulkily, "you've knocked Vi right out of my arms."

She looked round despairingly for the little dog which seemed to have disappeared in the long grass.

"Won't you please pick him up?" she pleaded.

"Not exactly in my line, you know," answered the other magnitude, "but I tell you what I'll do, if you'll stand still, perfectly still where you are, and let me take hold of your hand, I'll describe a circle!"

"Oh, aren't you clever!" cried the girl, clapping her hands. "What a lovely idea! You describe a circle all around me, and then we'll look at every weeny bit of it and we'll be sure to find Vi——"

She reached out her hand to the other magnitude who clasped it with an assumed intensity sufficient to retain it.

At this moment a third magnitude broke on the scene:—a huge oblong, angular figure, very difficult to describe, came revolving towards them.

"M," it shouted, "Emily, what are you doing?"

"My goodness," said the second magnitude in alarm, "it's M A M A."

I may say that the second instalment of Dr. Murray's fascinating romance will appear in the next number of the *Illuminated Bookworm*, the great adult-juvenile vehicle of the newer thought in which these theories of education are expounded further.

AN EVERY-DAY
EXPERIENCE

VII.—An Every-Day Experience

HE came across to me in the semi-silence room of the club.

"I had a rather queer hand at bridge last night," he said.

"Had you?" I answered, and picked up a newspaper.

"Yes. It would have interested you, I think," he went on.

"Would it?" I said, and moved to another chair.

"It was like this," he continued, following me: "I held the king of hearts——"

"Half a minute," I said; "I want to go and see what time it is." I went out and looked at the clock in the hall. I came back.

"And the queen and the ten——" he was saying.

"Excuse me just a second; I want to ring for a messenger."

I did so. The waiter came and went.

"And the nine and two small ones," he went on.

"Two small what?" I asked.

"Two small hearts," he said. "I don't remember which. Anyway, I remember very well indeed that I had the king and the queen and the jack, the nine, and two little ones."

"Half a second," I said, "I want to mail a letter."

When I came back to him, he was still murmuring:

"My partner held the ace of clubs and the queen. The jack was out, but I didn't know where the king was——"

"You didn't?" I said in contempt.

"No," he repeated in surprise, and went on murmuring:

"Diamonds had gone round once, and spades twice, and so I suspected that my partner was leading from weakness——"

"I can well believe it," I said—"sheer weakness."

"Well," he said, "on the sixth round the
168

lead came to me. Now, what should I have done? Finessed for the ace, or led straight into my opponent——"

"You want my advice," I said, "and you shall have it, openly and fairly. In such a case as you describe, where a man has led out at me repeatedly and with provocation, as I gather from what you say, though I myself do not play bridge, I should lead my whole hand at him. I repeat, I do not play bridge. But in the circumstances, I should think it the only thing to do."

TRUTHFUL ORATORY

VIII.—*Truthful Oratory, or What Our Speakers Ought to Say*

I

TRUTHFUL SPEECH GIVING THE REAL THOUGHTS OF A DISTINGUISHED GUEST AT THE FIFTIETH ANNIVERSARY BANQUET OF A SOCIETY

M R. CHAIRMAN AND GENTLEMEN: If there is one thing I abominate more than another, it is turning out on a cold night like this to eat a huge dinner of twelve courses and know that I have to make a speech on top of it. Gentlemen, I just feel stuffed. That's the plain truth of it. By the time we had finished that fish, I could have gone home satisfied. Honestly I could. That's as much as I usually eat. And by the time I had finished the rest of the food, I felt simply waterlogged, and I do still. More than that. The knowledge that I had to make a speech congratulating this society of yours on its fiftieth anniversary haunted and racked me all through the meal. I am not, in plain truth, the ready and brilliant speaker you take me for. That is a pure myth. If you could see the desperate home scene that goes on in my family when I am working up a speech, your minds would be at rest on that point.

I'll go further and be very frank with you. How this society has lived for fifty years, I don't know. If all your dinners are like this, Heaven help you. I've only the vaguest idea of what this society *is*, anyway, and what it does. I tried to get a constitution this afternoon but failed. I am sure from some of the faces that I recognise around this table that there must be good business reasons of some sort for belonging to this society. There's money in it,—mark my words,—for some of you or you wouldn't be here. Of course I quite understand that the President and the

officials seated here beside me come merely for
the self-importance of it. That, gentlemen, is
about their size. I realized that from their
talk during the banquet. I don't want to speak
bitterly, but the truth is they are *small* men
and it flatters them to sit here with two or
three blue ribbons pinned on their coats. But
as for me, I'm done with it. It will be fifty
years, please heaven, before this event comes
round again. I hope, I earnestly hope, that I
shall be safely under the ground.

II

THE SPEECH THAT OUGHT TO BE MADE BY A STATE GOVERNOR AFTER VISITING THE FALL EXPOSITION OF AN AGRICULTURAL SOCIETY

WELL, gentlemen, this Annual Fall Fair of
the Skedink County Agricultural Association
has come round again. I don't mind telling
you straight out that of all the disagreeable
jobs that fall to me as Governor of this State,

my visit to your Fall Fair is about the tough-
est.

I want to tell you, gentlemen, right here
and now, that I don't know anything about agriculture and I don't want to. My parents
were rich enough to bring me up in the city
in a rational way. I didn't have to do chores
in order to go to the high school as some of
those present have boasted that they did. My
only wonder is that they ever got there at all.
They show no traces of it.

This afternoon, gentlemen, you took me all
round your live-stock exhibit. I walked past,
and through, nearly a quarter of a mile of hogs.
What was it that they were called—Tam-
worths—Berkshires? I don't remember. But
all I can say, gentlemen, is,—phew! Just that.
Some of you will understand readily enough.
That word sums up my whole idea of your
agricultural show and I'm done with it.

No, let me correct myself. There was just
one feature of your agricultural exposition that
met my warm approval. You were good
enough to take me through the section of your

exposition called your Midway Pleasance. Let me tell you, sirs, that there was more real merit in that than all the rest of the show put together. You apologized, if I remember rightly, for taking me into the large tent of the Syrian Dancing Girls. Oh, believe me, gentlemen, you needn't have. Syria is a country which commands my profoundest admiration. Some day I mean to spend a vacation there. And, believe me, gentlemen, when I do go,— and I say this with all the emphasis of which I am capable,—I should not wish to be accompanied by such a set of flatheads as the officials of your Agricultural Society.

And now, gentlemen, as I have just received a fake telegram, by arrangement, calling me back to the capital of the State, I must leave this banquet at once. One word in conclusion: if I had known as fully as I do now how it feels to drink half a bucket of sweet cider, I should certainly never have come.

III

TRUTHFUL SPEECH OF A DISTRICT POLITICIAN TO A LADIES' SUF-FRAGE SOCIETY

LADIES: My own earnest, heartfelt conviction is that you are a pack of cats. I use the word "cats" advisedly, and I mean every letter of it. I want to go on record before this gathering as being strongly and unalterably opposed to Woman Suffrage until you get it. After that I favour it. My reasons for opposing the suffrage are of a kind that you couldn't understand. But all men,—except the few that I see at this meeting,—understand them by instinct.

As you may, however, succeed as a result of the fuss that you are making,—in getting votes, I have thought it best to come. Also,— I am free to confess,—I wanted to see what you looked like.

On this last head I am disappointed. Personally I like women a good deal fatter than

178

most of you are, and better looking. As I look around this gathering I see one or two of you that are not so bad, but on the whole not many. But my own strong personal predilection is and remains in favour of a woman who can cook, mend clothes, talk when I want her to, and give me the kind of admiration to which I am accustomed.

Let me, however, say in conclusion that I am altogether in sympathy with your movement to this extent. If you ever *do* get votes,—and the indications are that you will (blast you),— I want your votes, and I want all of them.

OUR LITERARY BUREAU

IX.—*Our Literary Bureau**

NOVELS READ TO ORDER
>   FIRST AID FOR THE
>>   BUSY MILLIONAIRE

No brains needed
>   No taste required
>>   Nothing but money
>>>   Send it to us

WE have lately been struck,—of course not dangerously,—by a new idea. A recent number of a well-known magazine contains an account of an American multimillionaire who, on account of the pressure of his brain power and the rush of his business, found it impossible to read the fiction of the day for himself. He therefore caused his secretaries to look

* This literary bureau was started by the author in the New York *Century*. It leaped into such immediate prominence that it had to be closed at once.

through any new and likely novel and make a rapid report on its contents, indicating for his personal perusal the specially interesting parts.

Realizing the possibilities coiled up in this plan, we have opened a special agency or bureau for doing work of this sort. Any over-busy multimillionaire, or superman, who becomes our client may send us novels, essays, or books of any kind, and will receive a report explaining the plot and pointing out such parts as he may with propriety read. If he can once find time to send us a postcard, or a postal cablegram, night or day, we undertake to assume all the further effort of reading. Our terms for ordinary fiction are one dollar per chapter; for works of travel, 10 cents per mile; and for political or other essays, two cents per page, or ten dollars per idea, and for theological and controversial work, seven dollars and fifty cents per cubic yard extracted. Our clients are assured of prompt and immediate attention.

Through the kindness of the Editor of the *Century* we are enabled to insert here a sample of our work. It was done to the order of a gentleman of means engaged in silver mining in Colorado, who wrote us that he was anxious to get "a holt" on modern fiction, but that he had no time actually to read it. On our assuring him that this was now unnecessary, he caused to be sent to us the monthly parts of a serial story, on which we duly reported as follows:

JANUARY INSTALMENT

Theodolite Gulch,
The Dip, Cañon County,
Colorado.

Dear Sir:

We beg to inform you that the scene of the opening chapter of the *Fortunes of Barbara Plynlimmon* is laid in Wales. The scene is laid, however, very carelessly and hurriedly and we expect that it will shortly be removed. We cannot, therefore, recommend it to your perusal. As there is a very fine passage describing the Cambrian Hills by moonlight, we enclose herewith a condensed table showing the mean altitude of the moon for the month of December in the latitude of Wales. The character of Miss Plynlimmon we find to be developed in conversation with her grandmother, which we think you had better not read. Nor are we prepared to endorse your reading the speeches of the Welsh peasantry which we find in this chapter, but we forward herewith in place of them a short glossary of Welsh synonyms which may aid you in this connection.

FEBRUARY INSTALMENT;

DEAR SIR:

We regret to state that we find nothing in the second chapter of the *Fortunes of Barbara Plynlimmon* which need be reported to you at length. We think it well, however, to apprise you of the arrival of a young Oxford student in the neighbourhood of Miss Plynlimmon's cottage, who is apparently a young man of means and refinement. We enclose a list of the principal Oxford Colleges.

We may state that from the conversation and manner of this young gentleman there is no ground for any apprehension on your part. But if need arises we will report by cable to you instantly.

The young gentleman in question meets Miss Plynlimmon at sunrise on the slopes of Snowdon. As the description of the meeting is very fine we send you a recent photograph of the sun.

MARCH INSTALMENT

DEAR SIR:

Our surmise was right. The scene of the story that we are digesting for you is changed. Miss Plynlimmon has gone to London. You will be gratified to learn that she has fallen heir to a fortune of £100,000, which we are happy to compute for you at $486,666 and 66 cents less exchange. On Miss Plynlimmon's arrival at Charing Cross Station, she is overwhelmed with that strange feeling of isolation felt in the surging crowds of a modern city. We therefore enclose a timetable showing the arrival and departure of all trains at Charing Cross.

APRIL INSTALMENT

DEAR SIR:

We beg to bring to your notice the fact that Miss Barbara Plynlimmon has by an arrangement made through her trustees become the inmate, on a pecuniary footing, in the household of a family of title. We are happy to inform you that her first appearance at dinner in evening dress was most gratifying: we can safely recommend you to read in this connection lines 4 and 5 and the first half of line 6 on page 100 of the book as enclosed. We regret to say that the Marquis of Slush and his eldest son Viscount Fitzbusé (courtesy title) are both addicted to drink. They have been drinking throughout the chapter. We are pleased to state that apparently the second son, Lord Radnor of Slush, who is away from home is not so addicted. We send you under separate cover a bottle of Radnor water.

MAY INSTALMENT

DEAR SIR:

We regret to state that the affairs of Miss Barbara Plynlimmon are in a very unsatisfactory position. We enclose three pages of the novel with the urgent request that you will read them at once. The old Marquis of Slush has made approaches towards Miss Plynlimmon of such a scandalous nature that we think it best to ask you to read them in full. You will note also that young Viscount Slush who is tipsy through whole of pages 121-125, 128-133, and part of page 140, has designs upon her fortune. We are sorry to see also that the Marchioness of Busé under the guise of friendship has insured Miss Plynlimmon's life and means to do away with her. The sister of the Marchioness, the Lady Dowager, also wishes to do away with her. The second housemaid who is tempted by her jewellery is also planning to do away with her. We feel that if this goes on she will be done away with.

JUNE INSTALMENT

DEAR SIR:

We beg to advise you that Viscount Fitz-busé, inflamed by the beauty and innocence of Miss Plynlimmon, has gone so far as to lay his finger on her (read page 170, lines 6-7). She resisted his approaches. At the height of the struggle a young man, attired in the costume of a Welsh tourist, but wearing the stamp of an Oxford student, and yet carrying himself with the unmistakable hauteur (we knew it at once) of an aristocrat, burst, or bust, into the room. With one blow he felled Fitz-busé to the floor; with another he clasped the girl to his heart.

"Barbara!" he exclaimed.

"Radnor," she murmured.

You will be pleased to learn that this is the second son of the Marquis, Viscount Radnor, just returned from a reading tour in Wales.

P. S. We do not know what he read, so we enclose a file of Welsh newspapers to date.

JULY INSTALMENT

We regret to inform you that the Marquis of Slush has disinherited his son. We grieve to state that Viscount Radnor has sworn that he will never ask for Miss Plynlimmon's hand till he has a fortune equal to her own. Meantime, we are sorry to say, he proposes to work.

AUGUST INSTALMENT

The Viscount is seeking employment.

SEPTEMBER INSTALMENT

The Viscount is looking for work.

OCTOBER INSTALMENT

The Viscount is hunting for a job.

NOVEMBER INSTALMENT

We are most happy to inform you that Miss Plynlimmon has saved the situation. Determined to be worthy of the generous love of Viscount Radnor, she has arranged to convey her entire fortune to the old family lawyer who acts as her trustee. She will thus become as poor as the Viscount and they can marry. The scene with the old lawyer who breaks into tears on receiving the fortune, swearing to hold and cherish it as his own is very touching. Meantime, as the Viscount is hunting for a job, we enclose a list of advertisements under the heading *Help Wanted—Males*.

DECEMBER INSTALMENT

You will be very gratified to learn that the fortunes of Miss Barbara Plynlimmon have come to a most pleasing termination. Her marriage with the Viscount Radnor was celebrated very quietly on page 231. (We enclose a list of the principal churches in London.) No one was present except the old family lawyer, who was moved to tears at the sight of the bright, trusting bride, and the clergyman who wept at the sight of the cheque given him by the Viscount. After the ceremony the old trustee took Lord and

Lady Radnor to a small wedding breakfast at an hotel
(we enclose a list). During the breakfast a sudden
faintness (for which we had been watching for ten
pages) overcame him. He sank back in his chair,
gasping. Lord and Lady Radnor rushed to him and
sought in vain to tighten his necktie. He expired
under their care, having just time to indicate in his
pocket a will leaving them his entire wealth.

This had hardly happened when a messenger
brought news to the Viscount that his brother, Lord
Fitz-busé had been killed in the hunting field, and
that he (meaning him, himself) had now succeeded
to the title. Lord and Lady Fitz-busé had hardly
time to reach the town house of the family when they
learned that owing to the sudden death of the old
Marquis (also, we believe, in the hunting field), they
had become the Marquis and the Marchioness of
Slush.

The Marquis and the Marchioness of Slush are still
living in their ancestral home in London. Their lives
are an example to all their tenantry in Piccadilly, the
Strand and elsewhere.

CONCLUDING NOTE

Dear Mr. Gulch:

We beg to acknowledge with many thanks your
cheque for one thousand dollars.

We regret to learn that you have not been able to
find time to read our digest of the serial story placed

with us at your order. But we note with pleasure that you propose to have the "essential points" of our digest "boiled down" by one of the business experts of your office,

Awaiting your commands,

We remain, etc., etc.

SPEEDING UP BUSINESS

X.—Speeding Up Business

WE were sitting at our editorial desk in our inner room, quietly writing up our week's poetry, when a stranger looked in upon us.

He came in with a burst,—like the entry of the hero of western drama coming in out of a snowstorm. His manner was all excitement. "Sit down," we said, in our grave, courteous way. "Sit down!" he exclaimed, "certainly not! Are you aware of the amount of time and energy that are being wasted in American business by the practice of perpetually sitting down and standing up again? Do you realize that every time you sit down and stand up you make a dead lift of"—he looked at us,— "two hundred and fifty pounds? Did you ever reflect that every time you sit down you have to get up again?" "Never," we said quietly, "we never thought of it." "You didn't!" he sneered. "No, you'd rather go on lifting 250 pounds through two feet,—an average of 500 foot-pounds, practically 62 kilowatts of wasted power. Do you know that by merely hitching a pulley to the back of your neck you could generate enough power to light your whole office?"

We hung our heads. Simple as the thing was, we had never thought of it. "Very good," said the Stranger. "Now, all American business men are like you. They don't think,—do you understand me? They don't think."

We realized the truth of it at once. We had never thought. Perhaps we didn't even know how.

"Now, I tell you," continued our visitor, speaking rapidly and with a light of wild enthusiasm in his face, "I'm out for a new campaign,—efficiency in business—speeding things up—better organization."

"But surely," we said, musingly, "we have seen something about this lately in the papers?" "Seen it, sir," he exclaimed, "I should say so. It's everywhere. It's a new movement. It's in the air. Has it never struck you how a thing like this can be seen in the air?"

Here again we were at fault. In all our lives we had never seen anything in the air. We had never even looked there. "Now," continued the Stranger, "I want your paper to help. I want you to join in. I want you to give publicity."

"Assuredly," we said, with our old-fashioned politeness. "Anything which concerns the welfare, the progress, if one may so phrase it——"

"Stop," said the visitor. "You talk too much. You're prosy. Don't talk. Listen to me. Try and fix your mind on what I am about to say."

We fixed it. The Stranger's manner became somewhat calmer. "I am heading," he said, "the new American efficiency movement. I have sent our circulars to fifty thousand representative firms, explaining my methods. I am receiving ten thousand answers a day"— here he dragged a bundle of letters out of his pocket—"from Maine, from New Hampshire, from Vermont,"—— "Massachusetts, Rhode Island, Connecticut," we murmured.

"Exactly," he said; "from every State in the Union—from the Philippines, from Porto Rico, and last week I had one from Canada." "Marvellous," we said; "and may one ask what your new methods are?"

"You may," he answered. "It's a proper question. It's a typical business question, fair, plain, clean, and even admitting of an answer. The great art of answering questions," he continued, "is to answer at once without loss of time, friction or delay in moving from place to place. I'll answer it."

"Do," we said.

"I will," said the Stranger. "My method is first: to stimulate business to the highest point by infusing into it everywhere the spirit of generous rivalry, of wholesome competition; by inviting each and every worker to outdo each and every other."

"And can they do it?" we asked, puzzled and yet fascinated. "Can they all do it?"

"They do, and they can," said the Stranger. "The proof of it is that they are doing it. Listen. Here is an answer to my circular No. 6,

Efficiency and Recompense, that came in this morning. It is from a steel firm. Listen."

The Stranger picked out a letter and read it.

DEAR SIR:

Our firm is a Steel Corporation. We roll rails. As soon as we read your circular on the Stimulus of Competition we saw that there were big things in it. At once we sent one of our chief managers to the rolling mill. He carried a paper bag in his hand. "Now boys," he said, "every man who rolls a rail gets a gum-drop." The effect was magical. The good fellows felt a new stimulus. They now roll out rails like dough. Work is a joy to them. Every Saturday night the man who has rolled most gets a blue ribbon; the man who has rolled the next most, a green ribbon; the next most a yellow ribbon, and so on through the spectroscope. The man who rolls least gets only a red ribbon. It is a real pleasure to see the brave fellows clamouring for their ribbons. Our output, after defraying the entire cost of the ribbons and the gum-drops, has increased forty per cent. We intend to carry the scheme further by allowing all the men who get a hundred blue ribbons first, to exchange them for the Grand Efficiency Prize of the firm,—a pink ribbon. This the winner will be entitled to wear whenever and wherever he sees fit to wear it.

The stranger paused for breath.

"Marvellous," we said. "There is no doubt the stimulus of keen competition——"

"Shut up," he said impatiently. "Let me explain it further. Competition is only part of it. An item just as big that makes for efficiency is to take account of the little things. It's the little things that are never thought of."

Here was another wonder! We realized that we had never thought of them. "Take an example," the Stranger continued. "I went into a hotel the other day. What did I see? Bell-boys being summoned upstairs every minute, and flying up in the elevators. Yes,—and every time they went up they had to come down again. I went up to the manager. I said, 'I can understand that when your guests ring for the bell-boys they have to go up. But why should they come down? Why not have them go up and never come down?' He caught the idea at once. That hotel is transformed. I have a letter from the manager stating that they find it fifty per cent. cheaper to hire new bell-boys instead of waiting for the old ones to come down."

"These results," we said, "are certainly marvellous. "You are most assuredly to be con-
gratulated on——"

"You talk too much," said the Stranger.
"Don't do it. Learn to listen. If a young man
comes to me for advice in business,—and they
do in hundreds, lots of them,—almost in tears
over their inefficiency,—I'd say, 'Young man,
never talk, listen; answer, but don't speak.'
But even all this is only part of the method.
Another side of it is technique."

"Technique?" we said, pleased but puzzled.

"Yes, the proper use of machine devices.
Take the building trade. I've revolutionized
it. Till now all the bricks even for a high
building were carried up to the mason in hods.
Madness! Think of the waste of it. By my
method instead of carrying the bricks to the
mason we take the mason to the brick,—lower
him on a wire rope, give him a brick, and up
he goes again. As soon as he wants another
brick he calls down, 'I want a brick,' and down
he comes like lightning."

"This," we said, "is little short of——"

"Cut it out. Even that is not all. Another thing bigger than any is organization. Half the business in this country is not organized. As soon as I sent out my circular, No. 4, HAVE YOU ORGANIZED YOUR BUSINESS! I got answers in thousands! Heartbroken, many of them. They had never thought of it! Here, for example, is a letter written by a plain man, a gardener, just an ordinary man, a plain man——"

"Yes," we said, "quite so."

"Well, here is what he writes:

DEAR SIR:

As soon as I got your circular I read it all through from end to end, and I saw that all my failure in the past had come from my not being organized. I sat and thought a long while and I decided that I would organize myself. I went right in to the house and I said to my wife, "Jane, I'm going to organize myself." She said, "Oh, John!"—and not another word, but you should have seen the look on her face. So the next morning I got up early and began to organize myself. It was hard at first but I stuck to it. There were times when I felt as if I couldn't do it. It seemed too hard. But bit by bit I did it and now, thank God, I am organized. I wish all men like me could know the pleasure I feel in being organized.

"Touching, isn't it?" said the Stranger. "But I get lots of letters like that. Here's another, also from a man, a plain man, working on his own farm. Hear what he says:

Dear Sir:

As soon as I saw your circular on *HOW TO SPEED UP THE EMPLOYEE* I felt that it was a big thing. I don't have any hired help here to work with me, but only father. He cuts the wood and does odd chores about the place. So I realized that the best I could do was to try to speed up father. I started in to speed him up last Tuesday, and I wish you could see him. Before this he couldn't split a cord of wood without cutting a slice off his boots. Now he does it in half the time.

"But there," the Stranger said, getting impatient even with his own reading, "I needn't read it all. It is the same thing all along the line. I've got the Method introduced into the Department Stores. Before this every customer who came in wasted time trying to find the counters. Now we install a patent springboard, with a mechanism like a catapult. As soon as a customer comes in an attendant puts him on the board, blindfolds him, and says, 'Where do you want to go?' 'Glove counter.' 'Oh, all right.' He's fired at it through the air. No time lost. Same with the railways. They're installing the Method, too. Every engineer who breaks the record from New York to Buffalo gets a glass of milk. When he gets a hundred glasses he can exchange them for a glass of beer. So with the doctors. On the new method, instead of giving a patient one pill a day for fourteen days they give him fourteen pills in one day. Doctors, lawyers, everybody,—in time, sir," said the Stranger, in tones of rising excitement, "you'll see even the plumbers——"

But just at this moment the door opened. A sturdy-looking man in blue entered. The Stranger's voice was hushed at once. The excitement died out of his face. His manner all of a sudden was meekness itself.

"I was just coming," he said.

"That's right, sir," said the man; "better

come along and not take up the gentleman's time."

"Good-bye, then," said the Stranger, with meek affability, and he went out.

The man in blue lingered behind for a moment.

"A sad case, sir," he said, and he tapped his forehead.

"You mean——" I asked.

"Exactly. Cracked, sir. Quite cracked; but harmless. I'm engaged to look after him, but he gave me the slip downstairs."

"He is under delusions?" we inquired.

"Yes, sir. He's got it into his head that business in this country has all gone to pieces, —thinks it must be reorganized. He writes letters about it all day and sends them to the papers with imaginary names. You may have seen some of them. Good day, sir."

We looked at our watch. We had lost just half an hour over the new efficiency. We turned back with a sigh to our old-fashioned task.

WHO IS ALSO WHO
A NEW POCKET
DICTIONARY

XI.—Who Is Also Who. A Companion Volume to Who's Who

NOTE BY THE EDITOR: *I do not quarrel with the contents of such valuable compendiums as "Who's Who," "Men and Women of the Time," etc., etc. But they leave out the really Representative People. The names that they include are so well known as to need no commentary, while those that they exclude are the very people one most wishes to read about. My new book is not arranged alphabetically, that order having given great offence in certain social circles.*

SMITH, J. EVERYMAN: born Kenoka Springs; educ. Kenoka Springs; present residence, The Springs, Kenoka; address, Kenoka Springs Post-Office; after leaving school threw himself (Oct. 1881) into college study; thrown out of it (April

1882); decided to follow the law; followed it
(1882); was left behind (1883); decided
(1884) to abandon it; abandoned it; resolved
(1885) to turn his energies to finance; turned
them (1886); kept them turned (1887); un-
turned them (1888); was offered position
(1889) as sole custodian of Mechanics' Insti-
tute, Kenoka Springs; decided (same date) to
accept it; accepted it; is there now; will be till
he dies.

FLINTLOCK, J. PERCUSSION: aged 87; war
veteran and pensioner; born, blank; educated,
blank; at outbreak of Civil War sprang to
arms; both sides; sprang Union first; entered
beef contract department of army of U. S.;
fought at Chicago, Omaha, and leading (beef)
centres of operation during the thickest of the
(beef) conflict; was under Hancock, Burnside,
Meade, and Grant; fought with all of them;
mentioned (very strongly) by all of them;
entered Confederate Service (1864); attached
(very much) to rum department of quarter-
master's staff; mentioned in this connection
(very warmly) in despatches of General Lee;

mustered out, away out, of army; lost from sight, 1865-1895; placed on pension list with rank of general, 1895; has stayed on, 1895-1915; obtained (on 6th Avenue) war medals and service clasps; publications—"My Campaigns under Grant," "Battles I have Saved," "Feeding an Army," "Stuffing the Public," etc., etc.; recreations, telling war stories; favorite amusement, showing war medals.

CROOK, W. UNDERHAND: born, dash; parents, double dash; educated at technical school; on graduation turned his attention to the problem of mechanical timelocks and patent safes; entered Sing-Sing, 1890; resident there, 1890-1893; Auburn, 1894, three months; various state institutions, 1895-1898; worked at profession, 1898-1899; Sing-Sing, 1900; professional work, 1901; Sing-Sing, 1902; profession, 1903, Sing-Sing; profession, Sing-Sing, etc., etc.; life appointment, 1908; general favorite, musical, has never killed anybody.

GLOOMIE, DREARY O'LEARY: Scotch dialect comedian and humorist; well known in Scot-

land; has standing offer from Duke of Suther-
land to put foot on estate.

Muck, O. Absolute: novelist; of low German extraction; born Rotterdam; educated
Muckendorf; escaped to America; long unrec-
ognized; leaped into prominence by writing
"The Social Gas-Pipe," a powerful indictment
of modern society, written in revenge for not
being invited to dinner; other works—"The
Sewerage of the Sea-Side," an arraignment of
Newport society, reflecting on some of his best
friends; "Vice and Super-Vice," a telling de-
nunciation of the New York police, written after they had arrested him; "White Ravens,"
an indictment of the clergy; "Black Crooks," an
indictment of the publishers, etc., etc.; has
arraigned and indicted nearly everybody.

Whyner, Egbert Ethelwind: poet, at
age of sixteen wrote a quatrain, "The Banquet
of Nebuchadnezzar," and at once left school;
followed it up in less than two years by a poem
in six lines "America"; rested a year and then
produced "Babylon, A Vision of Civilization,"
three lines; has written also "Herod, a Trag-

edy," four lines; "Revolt of Woman," two lines, and "The Day of Judgement," one line. Recreation, writing poetry.

ADULT, HON. UNDERDONE: address The Shrubbery, Hopton-under-Hyde, Rotherham-near-Pottersby, Potts, Hants, Hops, England (or words to that effect); organizer of the Boys' League of Pathfinders, Chief Commissioner of the Infant Crusaders, Grand Master of the Young Imbeciles; Major-General of the Girl Rangers, Chief of Staff of the Matron Mountain Climbers, etc.

ZFWINSKI, X. Z.: Polish pianist; plays all night; address 4,570 West 457 Street, Westside, Chicago West.

PASSIONATE
PARAGRAPHS

XII.—Passionate Paragraphs

(An extract from a recent (very recent) novel, illustrating the new beauties of language and ideas that are being rapidly developed by the twentieth century press.)

HIS voice as he turned towards her was taut as a tie-line.

"You don't love me!" he hoarsed, thick with agony. She had angled into a seat and sat sensing-rather-than-seeing him.

For a time she silenced. Then presently as he still stood and enveloped her,—

"Don't!" she thinned, her voice fining to a thread.

"Answer me," he gloomed, still gazing into-and-through her.

She half-heard half-didn't-hear him.

Night was falling about them as they sat thus

beside the river. A molten afterglow of iridescent saffron shot with incandescent carmine lit up the waters of the Hudson till they glowed like electrified uranium.

For a while they both sat silent,—looming.

"It had to be," she glumped.

"Why, why?" he barked. "Why should it have had to have been or (*more hopefully*) even be to be? Surely you don't mean because of *money?*"

She shuddered into herself.

The thing seemed to sting her (it hadn't really).

"Money!" she almost-but-not-quite-moaned. "You might have spared me that!"

He sank down and grassed.

. . . .

And after they had sat thus for another half-hour grassing and growling and angling and sensing one another, it turned out that all that he was trying to say was to ask if she would marry him.

And of course she said yes.

WEEJEE THE PET DOG

XIII.—*Weejee the Pet Dog. An Idyll of the Summer*

WE were sitting on the verandah of the Sopley's summer cottage.

"How lovely it is here," I said to my host and hostess, "and how still."

It was at this moment that Weejee, the pet dog, took a sharp nip at the end of my tennis trousers.

"Weejee!!" exclaimed his mistress with great emphasis, *"bad* dog! how dare you, sir! *bad* dog!"

"I hope he hasn't hurt you," said my host.

"Oh, it's nothing," I answered cheerfully. "He hardly scratched me."

"You know I don't think he means anything by it," said Mrs. Sopley.

"Oh, I'm *sure* he doesn't," I answered.

Weejee was coming nearer to me again as I spoke.

"Weejee!!" cried my hostess, "naughty dog, bad!"

"Funny thing about that dog," said Sopley, "the way he *knows* people. It's a sort of instinct. He knew right away that you were a stranger,—now, yesterday, when the butcher came, there was a new driver on the cart and Weejee knew it right away,—grabbed the man by the leg at once,—wouldn't let go. I called out to the man that it was all right or he might have done Weejee some harm."

At this moment Weejee took the second nip at my other trouser leg. There was a short *gur-r-r* and a slight mix-up.

"Weejee! Weejee!" called Mrs. Sopley. "How *dare* you, sir! You're just a *bad* dog!! Go and lie down, sir. I'm so sorry. I think, you know, it's your white trousers. For some reason Weejee simply *hates* white trousers. I do hope he hasn't torn them."

"Oh, no," I said; "it's nothing only a slight tear."

"Here, Weege, Weege," said Sopley, anxious to make a diversion and picking up a little chip of wood,—"chase it, fetch it out!" and he made the motions of throwing it into the lake.

"Don't throw it too far, Charles," said his wife. "He doesn't swim awfully well," she continued, turning to me, "and I'm always afraid he might get out of his depth. Last week he was ever so nearly drowned. Mr. Van Toy was in swimming, and he had on a dark blue suit (dark blue seems simply to infuriate Weejee) and Weejee just dashed in after him. He don't *mean* anything, you know, it was only the *suit* made him angry,—he really likes Mr. Van Toy,—but just for a minute we were quite alarmed. If Mr. Van Toy hadn't carried Weejee in I think he might have been drowned.

"By jove!" I said in a tone to indicate how appalled I was.

"Let me throw the stick, Charles," continued Mrs. Sopley. "Now, Weejee, look Weejee— here, good dog—look! look now (sometimes

223

Weejee simply won't do what one wants), here, Weejee; now, good dog!"

Weejee had his tail sideways between his legs and was moving towards me again.

"Hold on," said Sopley in a stern tone, "let me throw him in."

"Do be careful, Charles," said his wife.

Sopley picked Weejee up by the collar and carried him to the edge of the water—it was about six inches deep,—and threw him in,—with much the same force as, let us say, a pen is thrown into ink or a brush dipped into a pot of varnish.

"That's enough; that's quite enough, Charles," exclaimed Mrs. Sopley. "I think he'd better not swim. The water in the evening is always a little cold. Good dog, good doggie, good Weejee!"

Meantime "good Weejee" had come out of the water and was moving again towards me.

"He goes straight to you," said my hostess. "I think he must have taken a fancy to you."

He had.

To prove it, Weejee gave himself a rotary whirl like a twirled mop.

"Oh, I'm *so* sorry," said Mrs. Sopley. "I am. He's wetted you. Weejee, lie down, down, sir, good dog, bad dog, lie down!"

"It's all right," I said. "I've another white suit in my valise."

"But you must be wet through," said Mrs. Sopley. "Perhaps we'd better go in. It's getting late, anyway, isn't it?" And then she added to her husband, "I don't think Weejee ought to sit out here now that he's wet."

So we went in.

"I think you'll find everything you need," said Sopley, as he showed me to my room, "and, by the way, don't mind if Weejee comes into your room at night. We like to let him run all over the house and he often sleeps on this bed."

"All right," I said cheerfully, "I'll look after him."

That night Weejee came.

And when it was far on in the dead of night—so that even the lake and the trees were hushed in sleep, I took Weejee out and—but there is no need to give the details of it.

And the Sopleys are still wondering where Weejee has gone to, and waiting for him to come back, because he is so clever at finding his way.

But from where Weejee is, no one finds his way back.

.   .   .   .

SIDELIGHTS ON THE SUPERMEN

XIV.—Sidelights on the Supermen. An Interview with General Bernhardi.

H E came into my room in that modest, Prussian way that he has, clicking his heels together, his head very erect, his neck tightly gripped in his forty-two centimeter collar. He had on a Pickelhaube, or Prussian helmet, which he removed with a sweeping gesture and laid on the sofa.

So I knew at once that it was General Bernhardi.

In spite of his age he looked—I am bound to admit it—a fine figure of a man. There was a splendid fullness about his chest and shoulders, and a suggestion of rugged power all over him. I had not heard him on the stairs. He seemed to appear suddenly beside me.

"How did you get past the janitor?" I asked.

For it was late at night, and my room at college is three flights up the stairs.

"The janitor," he answered carelessly, "I killed him."

I gave a gasp.

"His resistance," the general went on, "was very slight. Apparently in this country your janitors are unarmed."

"You killed him?" I asked.

"We Prussians," said Bernhardi, "when we wish an immediate access anywhere, always kill the janitor. It is quicker: and it makes for efficiency. It impresses them with a sense of our Furchtbarkeit. You have no word for that in English, I believe?"

"Not outside of a livery stable," I answered.

There was a pause. I was thinking of the janitor. It seemed in a sort of way—I admit that I have a sentimental streak in me—a deplorable thing.

"Sit down," I said presently.

"Thank you," answered the General, but remained standing.

"All right," I said, "do it."

"Thank you," he repeated, without moving.

"I forgot," I said. "Perhaps you *can't* sit down."

"Not very well," he answered; "in fact, we Prussian officers"—here he drew himself up higher still—"never sit down. Our uniforms do not permit of it. This inspires us with a kind of Rastlosigkeit." Here his eyes glittered.

"It must," I said.

"In fact, with an Unsittlichkeit—an Unverschämtheit—with an Ein-für-alle-mal-un-durchaus——"

"Exactly," I said, for I saw that he was getting excited, "but pray tell me, General, to what do I owe the honour of this visit?"

The General's manner changed at once.

"Highly learned, and high-well-born-professor," he said, "I come to you as to a fellow author, known and honoured not merely in England, for that is nothing, but in Germany herself, and in Turkey, the very home of Culture."

I knew that it was mere flattery. I knew

231

that in this same way Lord Haldane had been so captivated as to come out of the Emperor's presence unable to say anything but "Sittlich-keit" for weeks; that good old John Burns had been betrayed by a single dinner at Potsdam, and that the Sultan of Turkey had been told that his Answers to Ultimatums were the wittiest things written since Kant's *Critique of Pure Reason*. Yet I was pleased in spite of myself.

"What!" I exclaimed, "they know my works of humour in Germany?"

"Do they know them?" said the General. "Ach! Himmel! How they laugh. That work of yours (I think I see it on the shelf behind you), *The Elements of Political Science*, how the Kaiser has laughed over it! And the Crown Prince! It nearly killed him!"

"I will send him the new edition," I said. "But tell me, General, what is it that you want of me?"

"It is about my own book," he answered. "You have read it?"

I pointed to a copy of *Germany and the Next*

War, in its glaring yellow cover—the very hue of Furchtbarkeit—lying on the table.

"You have read it? You have really read it?" asked the General with great animation.

"No," I said, "I won't go so far as to say that. But I have *tried* to read it. And I talk about it as if I had read it."

The General's face fell.

"You are as the others," he said. "They buy the book, they lay it on the table, they talk of it at dinner,—they say 'Bernhardi has prophesied this, Bernhardi foresaw that,' but read it,—nevermore."

"Still," I said, "you get the royalties."

"They are cut off. The perfidious British Government will not allow the treacherous publisher to pay them. But that is not my complaint."

"What is the matter, then?" I asked.

"My book is misunderstood. You English readers have failed to grasp its intention. It is not meant as a book of strategy. It is what you call a work of humour. The book is to laugh. It is one big joke."

"You don't say so!" I said in astonishment.

"Assuredly," answered the General. "Here" —and with this he laid hold of the copy of the book before me and began rapidly turning over the leaves—"let me set it out asunder for you, the humour of it. Listen, though, to this, where I speak of Germany's historical mission on page 73,—'No nation on the face of the globe is so able to grasp and appropriate all the elements of culture as Germany is?' What do you say to that? Is it not a joke? Ach, Himmel, how our officers have laughed over that in Belgium! With their booted feet on the mantelpiece as they read and with bottles of appropriated champagne beside them as they laugh."

"You are right, General," I said, "you will forgive my not laughing out loud, but you are a great humorist."

"Am I not? And listen further still, how I deal with the theme of the German character, —'Moral obligations such as no nation had ever yet made the standard of conduct, are laid down by the German philosophers.'"

"Good," I said, "gloriously funny; read me some more."

"This, then, you will like,—here I deal with the permissible rules of war. It is on page 236 that I am reading it. I wrote this chiefly to make laugh our naval men and our Zeppelin crews,—'A surprise attack, in order to be justified, must be made only on the armed forces of the state and not on its peaceful inhabitants. Otherwise the attack becomes a treacherous crime.' Eh, what?"

Here the General broke into roars of laughter.

"Wonderful," I said. "Your book ought to sell well in Scarborough and in Yarmouth. Read some more."

"I should like to read you what I say about neutrality, and how England is certain to violate our strategical right by an attack on Belgium and about the sharp measures that ought to be taken against neutral ships laden with contraband,—the passages are in Chapters VII and VIII, but for the moment I fail to lay the thumb on them."

"Give me the book, General," I said. "Now that I understand what you meant by it, I think I can show you also some very funny passages in it. These things, for example, that you say about Canada and the colonies,—yes, here it is, page 148,—'In the event of war the loosely-joined British Empire will break into pieces, and the colonies will consult their own interests,'—excellently funny,—and this again,— 'Canada will not permanently retain any trace of the English spirit,'—and this too,—'the Colonies can be completely ignored so far as the European theatre of war is concerned,'—and here again,—'Egypt and South Africa will at once revolt and break away from the empire,' —really, General, your ideas of the British Colonies are superbly funny. Mark Twain wasn't a circumstance on you."

"Not at all," said Bernhardi, and his voice reverted to his habitual Prussian severity, "these are not jokes. They are facts. It is only through the folly of the Canadians in not reading my book that they are not more widely

known. Even as it is they are exactly the views
of your great leader Heinrich Bauratze——"

"Who?" I said.

"Heinrich Bauratze, your great Canadian
leader——"

"Leader of what?"

"That I do not know," said Bernhardi. "Our
intelligence office has not yet heard what he
leads. But as soon as he leads anything we
shall know it. Meantime we can see from his
speeches that he has read my book. Ach! if
only your other leaders in Canada,—Sir Rob-
ert Laurier, Sir Osler Sifton, Sir Williams Bor-
den,—you smile, you do not realize that in
Germany we have exact information of everything: all that happens, we know it."

Meantime I had been looking over the leaves
of the book.

"Here at least," I said, "is some splendidly
humorous stuff,—this about the navy. 'The
completion of the Kiel Canal,' you write in
Chapter XII, 'is of great importance as it will
enable our largest battleships to appear unex-

pectedly in the Baltic and in the North Sea!' Appear unexpectedly! If they only would! How exquisitely absurd——"

"Sir!" said the General. "That is not to laugh. You err yourself. That is Furcht-barkeit. I did not say the book is all hu-mour. That would be false art. Part of it is humour and part is Furchbarkeit. That pas-sage is specially designed to frighten Admiral Jellicoe. And he won't read it! Potztau-sand, he won't read it!"—repeated the general, his eyes flashing and his clenched fist striking in the air—"What sort of combatants are these of the British Navy who refuse to read our war-books? The Kaiser's Heligoland speech! They never read a word of it. The Furcht-barkeit-Proklamation of August,—they never looked at it. The Reichstags-Rede with the printed picture of the Kaiser shaking hands with everybody,—they used it to wrap up sandwiches! What are they, then, Jellicoe and his men? They sit there in their ships and they read nothing! How can we get at them if they refuse to read? How can we frighten them away if they haven't culture enough to get frightened. Beim Himmel," shouted the General in great excitement——

But what more he said can never be known. For at this second a sudden catastrophe happened.

In his frenzy of excitement the General struck with his fist at the table, missed it, lost his balance and fell over sideways right on the point of his Pickelhaube which he had laid on the sofa. There was a sudden sound as of the ripping of cloth and the bursting of pneumatic cushions and to my amazement the General collapsed on the sofa, his uniform suddenly punctured in a dozen places.

"Schnapps," he cried, "fetch brandy."

"Great Heavens! General," I said, "what has happened?"

"My uniform!" he moaned, "it has burst! Give me Schnapps!"

He seemed to shrink visibly in size. His magnificent chest was gone. He was shrivelling into a tattered heap. He appeared as he lay there, a very allegory and illustration of

Prussian Furchtbarkeit with the wind going out of it.

"Fetch Schnapps,"—he moaned.

"There are no Schnapps here," I said, "this is McGill University."

"Then call the janitor," he said.

"You killed him," I said.

"I didn't. I was lying. I gave him a look that should have killed him, but I don't think it did. Rouse yourself from your chair, and call him——"

"I will," I said, and started up from my seat.

But as I did so, the form of General Bernhardi, which I could have sworn had been lying in a tattered heap on the sofa on the other side of the room, seemed suddenly to vanish from my eyes.

There was nothing before me but the empty room with the fire burned low in the grate, and in front of me an open copy of Bernhardi's book.

I must,—like many another reader,—have fallen asleep over it.

THE SURVIVAL OF THE FITTEST

XV.—The Survival of the Fittest

A BELL tinkled over the door of the little drug store as I entered it; which seemed strange in a lighted street of a great city.

But the little store itself, dim even in the centre and dark in the corners was gloomy enough for a country crossroads.

"I have to have the bell," said the man behind the counter, reading my thought, "I'm alone here just now."

"A toothbrush?" he said in answer to my question. "Yes, I guess I've got some somewhere round here." He was stooping under and behind his counter and his voice came up from below. "I've got some somewhere——" And then as if talking to himself he murmured from behind a pile of cardboard boxes, "I saw some Tuesday."

Had I gone across the street to the brilliant

premises of the Cut Rate Pharmaceutical where they burn electric light by the meterfull I should no sooner have said "tooth brush," than one of the ten clerks in white hospital jackets would have poured a glittering assortment over the counter—prophylactic, lactic and every other sort.

But I had turned in, I don't know why, to the little store across the way.

"Here, I guess these must be tooth brushes," he said, reappearing at the level of the counter with a flat box in his hand. They must have been presumably, or have once been,—at some time long ago.

"They're tooth brushes all right," he said, and started looking over them with an owner's interest.

"What is the price of them?" I asked.

"Well," the man said musingly, "I don't —jest—know. I guess it's written on them likely," and he began to look at the handles.

Over at the Pharmaceutical across the way the words "what price?" would have precipitated a ready avalanche of figures.

"This one seems to be seventy-five cents," he said and handed me one.

"Is it a good tooth brush?" I asked.

"It ought to be," he said, "you'd think, at that price."

He had no shop talk, no patter whatever.

Then he looked at the brush again, more closely.

"I don't believe it *is* seventy-five," he muttered, "I think it must be fifteen, don't you?"

I took it from his hand and looked and said, —for it is well to take an occasional step towards the Kingdom of Heaven,—that I was certain it was seventy-five.

"Well," said the man, "perhaps it is, my sight is not so good now. I've had too much to do here and the work's been using me up some."

I noticed now as he said this how frail he looked as he bent over his counter wrapping up the tooth brush.

"I've no sealing wax," he said, "or not handy."

"That doesn't matter," I answered, "just put it in the paper."

Over the way of course the tooth brush would have been done up almost instantaneously, in white enamel paper, sealed at the end and stamped with a label, as fast as the money paid for it went rattling along an automatic carrier to a cashier.

"You've been very busy, eh?" I asked.

"Well, not so much with customers," he said, "but with fixing up the place,"—here he glanced about him. Heaven only knows what he had fixed. There were no visible signs of it.

"You see I've only been in here a couple of months. It was a pretty tough looking place when I came to it. But I've been getting things fixed. First thing I did I put those two carboys in the window with the lights behind them. They show up fine, don't they?"

"Fine!" I repeated; so fine indeed that the dim yellow light in them reached three or four feet from the jar. But for the streaming light from the great store across the street, the windows of the little shop would have been invisible.

"It's a good location here," he said. Any one could have told him that it was the worst location within two miles.

"I'll get it going presently," he went on. "Of course it's uphill just at first. Being such a good location the rent is high. The first two weeks I was here I was losing five dollars a day. But I got those lights in the window and got the stock overhauled a little to make it attractive and last month I reckon I was only losing three dollars a day."

"That's better," I said.

"Oh, yes," he went on, and there was a clear glint of purpose in his eye that contrasted with his sunken cheeks. "I'll get it going. This last two weeks I'm not losing more than say two and a half a day or something like that? The custom is bound to come. You get a place fixed up and made attractive like this and people are sure to come sooner or later."

What it was that was fixed up, and wherein lay the attractiveness I do not know. It could not be seen with the outward eye. Perhaps after two months' work of piling dusty boxes now this way, now that, and putting little candles behind the yellow carboys to try the effect, some inward vision came that lighted the place up with an attractiveness wanting even in the glass and marble glitter of the Pharmacy across the way.

"Yes, sir," continued the man, "I mean to stay with it. I'll get things into shape here, fix it up a little more and soon I'll have it,"— here his face radiated with a vision of hope— "so that I won't lose a single cent."

I looked at him in surprise. So humble an ambition it had never been my lot to encounter.

"All that bothers me," he went on, "is my health. It's a nice business the drug business: I like it, but it takes it out of you. You've got to be alert and keen all the time; thinking out plans to please the custom when it comes. Often I don't sleep well nights for the rush of it."

I looked about the little shop, as gloomy and sleepful as the mausoleum of an eastern king, and wondered by what alchemy of the mind the little druggist found it a very vortex of activity.

"But I can fix my health," he returned—"I may have to get some one in here and go away for a spell. Perhaps I'll do it. The doctor was saying he thought I might take a spell off and think out a few more wrinkles while I'm away."

At the word "doctor" I looked at him more warmly, and I saw then what was plain enough to see but for the dim light of the little place, —the thin flush on the cheek, the hopeful mind, the contrast of the will to live and the need to die, God's little irony on man, it was all there plain enough to read. The "spell" for which the little druggist was going is that which is written in letters of sorrow over the sunlit desolation of Arizona and the mountains of Colorado.

. . . .

A month went by before I passed that way again. I looked across at the little store and

I read the story in its drawn blinds and the padlock on its door.

The little druggist had gone away for a spell. And they told me, on enquiry, that his journey had been no further than to the cemetery behind the town where he lies now, musing, if he still can, on the law of the survival of the fittest in this well-adjusted world.

And they say that the shock of the addition of his whole business to the great Pharmacy across the way scarcely disturbed a soda siphon.

THE FIRST NEWSPAPER

XVI.—The First Newspaper. A Sort of Allegory

HOW likes it you, Master Brenton?" said the brawny journeyman, spreading out the news sheet on a smooth oaken table where it lay under the light of a leaded window.

"A marvellous fair sheet," murmured Brenton Caxton, seventh of the name, "let me but adjust my glasses and peruse it further lest haply there be still aught in it that smacks of error."

"It needs not," said the journeyman, " 'tis the fourth time already from the press."

"Nay, nay," answered Master Brenton softly, as he adjusted his great horn-rimmed spectacles and bent his head over the broad damp news sheet before him. "Let us grudge no care in this. The venture is a new one and, meseems, a very parlous thing withal. 'Tis a venture that may easily fail and carry down our fortunes with it, but at least let it not be said that it failed for want of brains in the doing."

"Fail quotha!" said a third man, who had not yet spoken, old, tall and sour of visage and wearing a printer's leather apron. He had moved over from the further side of the room where a little group of apprentices stood beside the wooden presses that occupied the corner, and he was looking over the shoulder of Master Brenton Caxton.

"How can it do aught else? 'Tis a mad folly. Mark you, Master Brenton and Master Nick, I have said it from the first and let the blame be none of mine. 'Tis a mad thing you do here. See then," he went on, turning and waving his hand, "this vast room, these great presses, yonder benches and tools, all new, yonder vats of ink straight out of Flanders, how think you you can recover the cost of all this out of yonder poor sheets? Five and forty years have I followed this mystery of printing, ever since thy grandfather's day, Master Brenton, and never have I seen the like. What needed this great chamber when your grandfather and father were content with but a garret place, and yonder presses that can turn off four score copies in the compass of a single hour,—'Tis mad folly, I say."

The moment was an interesting one. The speakers were in a great room with a tall ceiling traversed by blackened beams. From the street below there came dimly through the closed casements the sound of rumbling traffic and the street cries of the London of the seventeenth century. Two vast presses of such colossal size that their wooden levers would tax the strength of the stoutest apprentice, were ranged against the further wall. About the room, spread out on oaken chairs and wooden benches, were flat boxes filled with leaden type, freshly molten, and a great pile of paper, larger than a man could lift, stood in a corner.

The first English newspaper in history was going to press. Those who in later ages,—editors, printers, and workers—have participated in the same scene, can form some idea of the hopes and fears, the doubts and the difficulties, with which the first newspaper was ushered into the world.

Master Brenton Caxton turned upon the last speaker the undisturbed look of the eye that sees far across the present into the years to come.

"Nay, Edward," he said, "you have laboured over much in the past and see not into the future. You think this chamber too great for our purpose? I tell you the time will come when not this room alone but three or four such will be needed for our task. Already I have it in my mind that I will divide even this room into portions, with walls shrewdly placed through its length and breadth, so that each that worketh shall sit as it were in his own chamber and there shall stand one at the door and whosoever cometh, to whatever part of our task his business appertains, he shall forthwith be brought to the room of him that hath charge of it. Cometh he with a madrigal or other light poesy that he would set out on the press, he shall find one that has charge of such matters and can discern their true value. Or, cometh he with news of aught that happens in the realm, so shall he be brought instant to the room of him that recordeth such events. Or, if so be, he would write a discourse on what seemeth him some wise conceit touching the public concerns, he shall find to his hand a convenient desk with ink and quills and all that he needeth to set it straightway on paper; thus shall there be a great abundance of written matter to our hand so that not many days shall elapse after one of our news sheets goes abroad before there be matter enough to fill another."

"Days!" said the aged printer, "think you you can fill one of these news sheets in a few days! Where indeed if you search the whole realm will you find talk enough in a single week to fill out this great sheet half an ell wide!"

"Ay, days indeed!" broke in Master Nicholas, the younger journeyman. "Master Brenton speaks truth, or less than truth. For not days indeed, but in the compass of a single day, I warrant you, shall we find the matter withal." Master Nicholas spoke with the same enthusiasm as his chief, but with less of the dreamer

in his voice and eye, and with more swift eager-
ness of the practical man.

"Fill it, indeed," he went on. "Why, Gad
Zooks! man! who knoweth what happenings
there are and what not till one essays the gathering of them! And should it chance that
there is nothing of greater import, no boar
hunt of his Majesty to record, nor the news of
some great entertainment by one of the Lords
of the Court, then will we put in lesser matter,
aye whatever comes to hand, the talk of his
Majesty's burgesses in the Parliament or any
such things."

"Hear him!" sneered the printer, "the talk
of his Majesty's burgesses in Westminster, for-
sooth! And what clerk or learned person
would care to read of such? Or think you that
His Majesty's Chamberlain would long bear
that such idle chatter should be bruited abroad.
If you can find no worthier thing for this our
news sheet than the talk of the Burgesses, then
shall it fail indeed. Had it been the speech of
the King's great barons and the bishops 'twere
different. But dost fancy that the great bar-

ons would allow that their weighty discourses be reduced to common speech so that even the vulgar may read it and haply here and there fathom their very thought itself,—and the bishops, the great prelates, to submit their ideas to the vulgar hand of a common printer, framing them into mere sentences! 'Tis unthinkable that they would sanction it!"

"Aye," murmured Caxton in his dreaming voice, "the time shall come, Master Edward, when they will not only sanction it but seek it."

"Look you," broke in Master Nick, "let us have done with this talk? Whether there be enough happenings or not enough,"—and here he spoke with a kindling eye and looked about him at the little group of apprentices and printers, who had drawn near to listen, "if there be not enough, then will I *make things happen*. What is easier than to tell of happenings forth of the realm of which no man can know,—some talk of the Grand Turk and the war that he makes, or some happenings in the New Land found by Master Columbus. Aye," he went on, warming to his words and not knowing that he embodied in himself the first birth on earth of the telegraphic editor,—"and why not. One day we write it out on our sheet 'The Grand Turk maketh disastrous war on the Bulgars of the North and hath burnt divers of their villages.' And that hath no sooner gone forth than we print another sheet saying, 'It would seem that the villages be not burnt but only scorched, nor doth it appear that the Turk burnt them but that the Bulgars burnt divers villages of the Turk and are sitting now in his mosque in the city of Hadrian.' Then shall all men run to and fro and read the sheet and question and ask, 'Is it thus?' And, 'Is it thus?' and by very uncertainty of circumstances, they shall demand the more curiously to see the news sheet and read it."

"Nay, nay, Master Nick," said Brenton, firmly, "that will I never allow. Let us make it to ourselves a maxim that all that shall be said in this news sheet, or 'news paper,' as my conceit would fain call it, for be it not made of paper (here a merry laugh of the apprentices greeted the quaint fancy of the Master), shall be of ascertained verity and fact indisputable. Should the Grand Turk make war and should the rumour of it come to these isles, then will we say 'The Turk maketh war,' and should the Turk be at peace, then we will say 'The Turk it doth appear is now at peace.' And should no news come, then shall we say 'In good sooth we know not whether the Turk destroyeth the Bulgars or whether he doth not, for while some hold that he harasseth them sorely, others have it that he harasseth them not, whereby we are sore put to it to know whether there be war or peace, nor do we desire to vex the patience of those who read by any further discourse on the matter, other than to say that we ourselves are in doubt what be and what be not truth, nor will we any further speak of it other than this.' "

Those about Caxton listened with awe to this speech. They did not,—they could not know,—that this was the birth of the Leading Article, but there was something in the strangely fascinating way in which their chief enlarged upon his own ignorance that foreshowed to the meanest intelligence the possibilities of the future.

Nicholas shook his head.

" 'Tis a poor plan, Master Brenton," he said, "the folk wish news, give them the news. The more thou givest them, the better pleased they are and thus doth the news sheet move from hand to hand till it may be said (if I too may coin a phrase) to increase vastly its 'circulation'——"

"In sooth," said Master Brenton, looking at Nicholas with a quiet expression that was not exempt from a certain slyness, "there I do hold thou art in the wrong, even as a matter of craft or policie. For it seems to me that if our paper speaketh first this and then that but hath no fixed certainty of truth, sooner or later will all its talk seem vain, and no man will heed it. But if it speak always the truth, then sooner or later shall all come to believe it and say of any happening, 'It standeth written in the paper, therefore it is so.' And here I charge you all that have any part in this new venture," continued Master Brenton, looking about the room at the listening faces and speaking with great seriousness, "let us lay it to our hearts that our maxim shall be truth and truth alone. Let no man set his hand to aught that shall go upon our presses save only that which is assured truth. In this way shall our venture ever be pleasing to the Most High, and I do verily believe,"—and here Caxton's voice sank lower as if he were thinking aloud,—"in the long run, it will be mighty good for our circulation."

The speaker paused. Then turning to the broad sheet before him, he began to scan its columns with his eye. The others stood watching him as he read.

"What is this, Master Edward," he queried presently, "here I see in this first induct, or column, as one names it, the word King fairly and truly spelled. Lower down it standeth Kyng, and yet further in the second induct Kynge, and in the last induct where there is talk of His Majesty's marvelous skill in the French game of palm or tennis, lo the word stands Quhyngge! How sayeth thou?"

"Wouldst have it written always in but one

and the same way?" asked the printer in astonishment.

"Aye, truly," said Caxton.

"With never any choice, or variation to suit the fancy of him who reads so that he who likes it written King may see it so, and yet also he who would prefer it written in a freer style, or Quhyngge, may also find it so and thus both be pleased."

"That will I never have!" said Master Brenton firmly, "dost not remember, friend, the old tale in the fabula of Æsopus of him who would please all men. Here will I make another maxim for our newspaper. All men we cannot please, for in pleasing one belike we run counter to another. Let us set our hand to write always without fear. Let us seek favour with none. Always in our news sheet we will seek to speak dutifully and with all reverence of the King his Majesty: let us also speak with all respect and commendation of His Majesty's great prelates and nobles, for are they not the exalted of the land? Also I would have it that we say nothing harsh against our wealthy merchants and burgesses, for hath not the Lord prospered them in their substances. Yea, friends, let us speak ever well of the King, the clergy, the nobility and of all persons of wealth and substantial holdings. But beyond this"— here Brenton Coxton's eye flashed,—"let us speak with utter fearlessness of all men. So shall we be, if I may borrow a mighty good word from Tacitus his Annals, of a complete independence, hanging on to no man. In fact our venture shall be an independent newspaper."

The listeners felt an instinctive awe at the words, and again a strange prescience of the future made itself felt in every mind. Here for the first time in history was being laid down that fine, fearless creed that has made the independent press what it is.

Meantime Caxton continued to glance his eye over the news sheet, murmuring his comments on what he saw,—"Ah! vastly fine, Master Nicholas,—this of the sailing of His Majesty's ships for Spain,—and this, too, of the Doge of Venice, his death, 'tis brave reading and maketh a fair discourse. Here also this likes me, 'tis shrewdly devised," and here he placed his finger on a particular spot on the news sheet,—"here in speaking of the strange mishap of my Lord Arundel, thou useth a great S for strange, and setteth it in a line all by itself whereby the mind of him that reads is suddenly awakened, alarmed as it were by a bell in the night. 'Tis good. 'Tis well. But mark you, friend Nicholas, try it not too often, nor use your great letters too easily. In the case of my Lord Arundel, it is seemly, but for a mishap to a lesser person, let it stand in a more modest fashion."

There was a pause. Then suddenly Caxton looked up again.

"What manner of tale is this! What strange thing is here! In faith, Master Nicholas, whence hast thou so marvelous a thing! The whole world must know of it. Harken ye all to this!

" 'Let all men that be troubled of aches, spavins, rheums, boils, maladies of the spleen or humours of the blood, come forthwith to the sign of the Red Lantern in East Cheap. There

shall they find one that hath a marvelous remedy for all such ailments, brought with great
dangers and perils of the journey from a far
distant land. This wonderous balm shall
straightway make the sick to be well and the
lame to walk. Rubbed on the eye it restoreth
sight and applied to the ear it reviveth the hearing. 'Tis the sole invention of Doctor Gusta-
vus Friedman, sometime of Göttingen and
brought by him hitherwards out of the sheer
pity of his heart for them that be afflicted, nor
shall any other fee be asked for it save only
such a light and tender charge as shall defray
the cost of Doctor Friedman his coming and
going.' "

Caxton paused and gazed at Master Nicholas in wonder. "Whence hadst thou this?"

Master Nicholas smiled.

"I had it of a chapman, or travelling doctor,
who was most urgent that we set it forth
straightway on the press."

"And is it true?" asked Caxton; "thou hast
it of a full surety of knowledge?"

Nicholas laughed lightly.

"True or false, I know not," he said, "but the fellow was so curious that we should print it that he gave me two golden laurels and a new sovereign on the sole understanding that we should set it forth in print."

There was deep silence for a moment.

"He *payeth* to have it printed!" said Caxton, deeply impressed.

"Aye," said Master Nicholas, "he payeth and will pay more. The fellow hath other balms equally potent. All of these he would admonish, or shall I say advert, the public."

"So," said Caxton, thoughtfully, "he wishes to make, if I may borrow a phrase of Albertus Magnus, an advertisement of his goods."

"Even so," said Nicholas.

"I see," said the Master, "he payeth us. We advert the goods. Forthwith all men buy them. Then hath he more money. He payeth us again. We advert the goods more and still he payeth us. That would seem to me, friend Nick, a mighty good busyness for us."

"So it is," rejoined Nicholas, "and after him others will come to advert other wares until belike a large part of our news sheet,—who knows? the whole of it, perhaps, shall be made up in the merry guise of advertisements."

Caxton sat silent in deep thought.

"But Master Caxton"—cried the voice of a young apprentice, a mere child, as he seemed, with fair hair and blue eyes filled with the native candour of unsullied youth,—"is this tale true!"

"What sayest thou, Warwick?" said the master printer, almost sternly.

"Good master, is the tale of the wonderous balm true?"

"Boy," said Caxton, "Master Nicholas, hath even said, we know not if it is true."

"But didst thou not charge us," pleaded the boy, "that all that went under our hand into the press should be truth and truth alone?"

"I did," said Caxton thoughtfully, "but I spoke perhaps somewhat in overhaste. I see that we must here distinguish. Whether this is true or not we cannot tell. But it is *paid for,* and that lifts it, as who should say, out of the domain of truth. The very fact that it is paid for giveth it, as it were, a new form of merit, a verity altogether its own."

"Ay, ay," said Nicholas, with a twinkle in his shrewd eyes, "entirely its own."

"Indeed so," said Caxton, "and here let us make to ourselves another and a final maxim of guidance. All things that any man will pay for, these we will print, whether true or not, for that doth not concern us. But if one cometh here with any strange tale of a remedy or aught else and wishes us to make advertisement of it and hath no money to pay for it, then shall he be cast forth out of this officina, or office, if I may call it so, neck and crop into the street. Nay, I will have me one of great strength ever at the door ready for such castings."

A murmur of approval went round the group.

Caxton would have spoken further but at the moment the sound of a bell was heard booming in the street without.

" 'Tis the Great Bell," said Caxton, "ringing out the hour of noon. Quick, all of you to your task. Lay me the forms on the press and speed me the work. We start here a great adventure. Mark well the maxims I have given you, and God speed our task."

And in another hour or so, the prentice boys of the master printer were calling in the streets the sale of the first English newspaper.

IN THE GOOD TIME
AFTER THE WAR

XVII.—In the Good Time After the War*

THE Prime Minister in rising said that he thought the time had now come when the House might properly turn its attention again to domestic affairs. The foreign world was so tranquil that there was really nothing of importance which need be brought to the attention of the House. Members, however, would, perhaps, be glad to learn incidentally that a new and more comfortable cage had been supplied for the ex-German Emperor, and that the ex-Crown Prince was now showing distinct signs of intelligence, and was even able to eat quite quietly out of his keeper's hand. Members would be gratified to know that at last the Hohenzollern family were able to abstain from snapping at

* An extract from a London newspaper of 1916.

the hand that fed them. But he would now turn to the subject of Home Rule.

Here the House was seen to yawn noticeably, and a general lack of interest was visible, especially among the Nationalist and Ulster members. A number of members were seen to rise as if about to move to the refreshment-room. Mr. John Redmond and Sir Edward Carson were seen walking arm in arm towards the door.

The Prime Minister. "Will the members kindly keep their seats? We are about to hold a discussion on Home Rule. Members will surely recall that this form of discussion was one of our favourite exercises only a year or so ago. I trust that members have not lost interest in the subject." (*General laughter among the members, and cries of "Cut it out!" "What is it?"*)

The Prime Minister (*with some asperity*). "Members are well aware what Home Rule meant. It was a plan—or rather it was a scheme—that is to say, it was an act of parliament, or I should say a bill, in fact, Mr.

Speaker, I don't mind confessing that, not having my papers with me, I am unable to inform the House just what Home Rule was. I think, perhaps, the Ex-Minister of Munitions has a copy of last year's bill."

Mr. Lloyd George rising, with evident signs of boredom. "The House will excuse me. I am tired. I have been out all day aeroplaning with Mr. Churchill and Mr. Bonar Law, with a view to inspect the new national training camp. I had the Home Rule Bill with me along with the Welsh Disestablishment Bill and the Land Bill, and I am afraid that I lost the whole bally lot of them; dropped them into the sea or something. I hope the Speaker will overlook the term 'bally.' It may not be parliamentary."

Mr. Speaker (laughing). "Tut, tut, never mind a little thing like that. I am sure that after all that we have gone through together, the House is quite agreed that a little thing like parliamentary procedure doesn't matter."

Mr. Lloyd George (humbly). "Still I am sorry for the term. I'd like to withdraw it. I

am afraid I used,—I mean in the old days,—
to be a little bit too harsh in my speech, too
cutting."

Chorus of Tory members. "No, no, never."

Mr. Lloyd George. "It is kind of the members on the opposite side of the House—
(cries of 'order,' 'order'). I beg the House's
pardon, I had forgotten that under the new
rule all the members sit together as they please.
But I was going to say that, as to this business
of Home Rule, I think the Speaker should ask
Mr. Redmond and Sir Edward Carson what
they think about it. Personally I don't care an
army button about it either way."

*Sir Edward Carson (turning to Mr. Red-
mond).* "Will you speak first, John?"

Mr. Redmond. "No, no, my dear Edward,
you speak. I much prefer to listen to you.
You've got a way of talking that I could never
hope to imitate. I could listen to you all day."

Sir Edward. "My dear old fellow! Talk
of my oratory! Do you think I shall ever forget, or any other Irishman ever forget, that
speech you made in August of 1914, when you

said that, the man who would lift his hand against the British Empire must deal first with the united people of Ireland?"

He clasps his hand. There is a moment of general emotion which is saved by the Speaker saying: "Will all the members kindly rise and sing 'It's a Long Way to Tipperary'?"

The Speaker (after the song). "Sir Edward, I think you had better say something. The House expects it."

Sir Edward Carson. "In that case, Mr. Speaker, I want to say just this: I don't care and none of my constituents or supporters care, whether we have a Home Rule Parliament in Ireland or not. But after what I've seen, and what I've heard of the Irish Nationalists in the war; when I think of them in that first struggle of the Retreat; when I see them as they lined the trenches in Belgium, defiant of hardship, reckless of danger, heedless of life itself, so that the flag of the Empire might move but one yard further against the foe, then, I say this, that neither I nor any Irishman will consent to any measure of government that shall

279

separate or distinguish in any degree the men
of Ulster from the men of Tipperary, and the
heart of Belfast from the heart of Dublin."
(Loud cheers.)

Mr. Redmond (springing forward). "And
I'll say this: Not I, nor any man of Ireland,
Dublin, Belfast, or Connaught will ever set
our hands or names to any bill that shall separate Ireland in any degree from the rest of the
Empire. Work out, if you like, a new scheme
of government. If the financial clauses are intricate, get one of your treasury clerks to solve
them. If there's trouble in arranging your ex-
cise on your customs, settle it in any way you
please. But it is too late now to separate England and Ireland. We've held the flag of the
Empire in our hand. We mean to hold it in
our grasp forever. We have seen its colours
tinged a brighter red with the best of Ireland's
blood, and that proud stain shall stay forever
as the symbol of the unity of Irish and the
English people."

*(Loud cheers ring through the House; sev-
eral members rise in great excitement, all*
280

*shouting and speaking together.)   There is
heard the voice of Mr. Angus McCluskey,
Member for the Hebrides, calling*—"And ye'll
no forget Scotland, me lad, when you talk of
unity! Do you mind the Forty-Second, and the
London Scottish in the trenches of the Aisne?
Wha carried the flag of the Empire then?
Unity, ma friends, ye'll never break it. It may
involve a wee bit sacrifice for Scotland finan-
cially speaking. I'll no say no to a reveesion
of the monetairy terms, if ye suggest it,—but
for unita—Scotland and the Empire, now and
forever!"

*A great number of members have risen in
their seats. Mr. Open Ap Owen Glendower is
calling: "Aye and Wales! never forget Wales."
Mr. Trevelyan Trendinning of Cornwall has
started singing* "And shall Trelawney Die?"—
while the deep booming of "Rule Britannia"
*from five hundred throats ascends to the very
rafters of the House.*

*The Speaker laughing and calling for order,
while two of the more elderly clerks are beating with the mace on the table,*—"Gentlemen,

gentlemen, I have a proposal to make. I have just learned that there is at the Alhambra in Leicester Square, a real fine moving picture show of the entrance of the Allies into Berlin. Let's all go to it. We can leave a committee of the three youngest members to stay behind and draw up a new government for Ireland. Even they can't go wrong now as to what we want."

Loud Cheers as the House empties, singing "It was a Long Way to Tipperary, but the way lay through Berlin."

THE END

Arcadian Adventures
With the Idle Rich

BY
STEPHEN LEACOCK
Author of "Nonsense Novels," "Sunshine Sketches," etc.

12mo   *Cloth*   *$1.25 net*

JOHN LANE COMPANY, *Publishers,* **NEW YORK**

BOOKS BY STEPHEN LEACOCK

BEHIND THE BEYOND
AND OTHER CONTRIBUTIONS TO HUMAN KNOWLEDGE
ILLUSTRATED BY A. H. FISH

"In Mr. Stephen Leacock we have a humorist of very marked individuality. His new book, 'Behind the Beyond,' is undeniably mirth-provoking. Dull must be the soul who does not find something to laugh at in the five sketches called 'Familiar Incidents' —visits to the photographer, the dentist, the barber, and so on."
—*Boston Transcript.*

"Out of apparently very abundant experience of life both off and on the stage, Mr. Leacock has presented an uncommonly clever satire on the modern problem play and some short stories of familiar happenings that are treated with a delightful sense of humor."—*Baltimore Sun.*

NONSENSE NOVELS

"A knack of story telling, a gift of caricature, and a full sense of humor are displayed in these ten nonsense novels."
—*Washington Star.*

"Even the most loyal admirers of Sherlock Holmes and his marvelous feats of induction and deduction will hardly grudge a smile of appreciation to Stephen Leacock."—*New York Sun.*

"Mr. Leacock bids fair to rival the immortal Lewis Carroll in combining the irreconcilable—exact science with perfect humor —and making the amusement better the instruction."
—*Pall Mall Gazette.*

BOOKS BY STEPHEN LEACOCK

LITERARY LAPSES

"This book deserves a wide reading, for it is spontaneous, fresh, and unforced."—*Chicago Tribune*.

"Philosophic humor, amusing and bubbling over with the froth of a delightful, good-natured cynicism."
—*Philadelphia Public Ledger*.

"Mr. Stephen Leacock is not only that very rare thing, a humorist, but that still rarer thing, a humorist in high spirits. A collection of good things which will entertain any human being who appreciates the humor of high spirits. The sketch entitled 'How to be a Doctor' no really serious medical student can afford to be without."—*Onlooker* (*London*).

SUNSHINE SKETCHES OF A LITTLE TOWN

"Humor, unspoiled by irony, satire, or even the gentlest raillery, characterizes this book. And few books are more suitably entitled, for these sketches do shed into the cracks and crannies of the heart glorious sunshine, the companion of pure mirth." —*Chicago Record-Herald*.

"Mr. Leacock's fun is always good-natured, and therefore doubly enjoyable."—*New York Times*.

"We cannot recall a more laughable book."—*Pall Mall Gazette*.